CH00688626

Life

INTERMEDIATE

Helen Stephenson

Life Intermediate Workbook

Helen Stephenson

Publisher: Jason Mann

Publishing Consultant: Karen Spiller

Editorial Project Manager: Karen Spiller

Development Editor: Liz Driscoll

Contributing Writer: Nick Kenny
 (IELTs practice test)

Strategic Marketing Manager:
 Michelle Cresswell

Project Editor: Amy Borthwick

Production Controller: Elaine Willis

National Geographic Liaison: Leila Hishmeh

Cover design: Vasiliki Christoforidou

Text design: Vasiliki Christoforidou

Compositor: Q2AMedia Ltd

Audio: Prolingua Productions

ISBN: 978-1-133-31688-6

National Geographic Learning
Cheriton House, North Way, Andover, Hampshire SP10 5BE
United Kingdom

Cengage Learning is a leading provider of customised learning solutions with office locations around the globe, including Singapore, the United Kingdom, Australia, Mexico, Brazil and Japan. Locate our local office at **international.cengage.com/region**

Cengage Learning products are represented in Canada by Nelson Education Ltd.

Visit National Geographic Learning at **ngl.cengage.com**
Visit our corporate website at **www.cengage.com**

CREDITS

Although every effort has been made to contact copyright holders prior to publication, this has not always been possible. If notified, the publisher will undertake to rectify any errors or omissions at the earliest opportunity.

Text:
The publisher would like to thank the following sources for permission to reproduce their copyright protected text:

National Geographic for extracts adapted from "Red Alert", *National Geographic Magazine*, September 2007; "Field Notes" by Bryan Skerry, http://ngm.nationalgeographic.com; "A Master Storyteller" by Keith Bellows, http://travel.nationalgeographic.com; "Boyd recalls a memorable meal he hand-picked with an Aborigine guide in the Australian outback", by Boyd Manson, www.nationalgeographic.com; "Bob Ballard, Marine Explorer", www.nationalgeographic.com; "Jodi Cobb, Photographer", www.nationalgeographic.com; "Børge Ousland, Polar Explorer", www.nationalgeographic.com; "Timbuktu", http://travel.nationalgeographic.com; Urban Visionary" by Keith Bellows, http://travel.nationalgeographic.com; "Ten Weirdest New Animals of 2010: Editors' Picks: Yoda Bat & Squid worm", http://news.nationalgeographic.com; "Nine Fish With "Hands" Found to Be New Species: See Spot Walk", http://news.nationalgeographic.com; "Predictable Passwords" by Catherine Zuckerman, http://ngm.nationalgeographic.com; "What can the body take?", *National Geographic Magazine*, October 2009; "Our Brains Are Already 'Limitless" by Marc Silver, 18 March 2011, http://blogs.ngm.com; "Paula Kahumbu Wildlife Conservationist", http://www.nationalgeographic.com; "Ken Banks Mobile Technology Innovator", http://www.nationalgeographic.com; Figure ID 1276023 by Oliver Uberti and extract from "As the word turns" by Jeremy Berlin, *National Geographic Magazine*, December 2009, copyright © National Geographic. Reproduced with permission; Vantha Tuy and National Geographic for material about Tuy Sereivathana, Conservationist, http://www.nationalgeographic.com. Reproduced with permission. IELTs practice test: Directgov for extracts from "Internet, mail order and telephone shopping", http://www.direct.gov.uk/en/Governmentcitizensandrights/Consumerrights/Situationsthatcanchangeyourconsumerrights/DG_183048, © Crown copyright, 2011; What Consumer for extracts adapted from "Buying Online" http://whatconsumer.co.uk/buying-online/, copyright © What Consumer 2012; The Independent for an extract adapted from `Dig finds earliest evidence of humans in Australia' by Kathy Marks, *The Independent on Sunday* 14 November 2010 p.3, copyright © The Independent, 2010; and Ed Douglas for material from `Sprinting up Mountains' by Ed Douglas published in *The | Financial Times Weekend* 1 October 2011, copyright © Ed Douglas.

Photos:
The publisher would like to thank the following sources for permission to reproduce their copyright protected photos:

Cover: George Steinmetz/National geographic Image Collection

Inside: pp 4 (Rebecca Hale/National Geographic Image Collection), 5 l (Shutterstock), 5 br (Shutterstock), 6 (bibikoff/iStockphoto), 8 tl (Shutterstock), 8 cl (Ratstuben/iStockphoto), 12 (Richard Nowitz/National Geographic Image Collection), 15 (Alan Welner/AP/Press Association Images), 16 (Shutterstock), 18 (EPA: European Pressphoto Agency b.v./Alamy), 20 3 (Brian J. Skerry/National Geographic Image Collection), 22 (Gregory Bull/AP/Press Association Images), 23 (Schalk Van Zuydam/AP/Press Association Images), 24 (Shutterstock), 25 (Shutterstock), 26 (Stephen Barnes/Titanic/Alamy), 28 -029 (John Stanmeyer LLC/National Geographic Image Collection), 30 (Catherine Karnow/National Geographic Image Collection), 32 (Yuri_Arcurs/iStockphoto), 33 (Shutterstock), 34 (Shutterstock), 37 (Boyd Matson), 38 tr (Shutterstock), 38 br (Shutterstock), 39 (Getty Images), 40 (Shutterstock), 41 (JoeFox Tenerife/Alamy), 42 (Shutterstock), 45 tl (Bill Bachman/Alamy), 45 cl (Davo Blair/Alamy), 47 (Shutterstock), 48 (Pete McBride/National Geographic Image Collection), 49 (David Burnett/National Geographic Image Collection), 50 (Scott Hortop/Alamy), 53 t (Shutterstock), 53 br (davincidig/iStockphoto), 54 (Shutterstock), 55 (Sean Caffrey/Lonely Planet Images/Getty Images), 58 (Shutterstock), 61 tl (AlamyCelebrity/Alamy), 61 cr (Piotr Naskrecki/Minden Pictures), 61 bl (Laurence Madin/Woods Hole Oceanographic Institution), 62 l (Shutterstock), 64 1 (Sandro Campardo), 64 2 (Shutterstock), 64 3 (Shutterstock), 64 4 (Shutterstock), 65 l (Shutterstock), 65 r (Richmatts/iStockphoto), 66 (Shutterstock), 70 tr (Randy Olson/National Geographic Image Collection), 70 br (Joe Petersburger/National Geographic Image Collection), 71 bl (Richard Nowitz/National Geographic Image Collection), 71 bc (Shutterstock), 71 ur (Shutterstock), 71 br (Shutterstock), 72 ul (Shutterstock), 72 ur (Shutterstock), 72 bl (Shutterstock), 72 br (Shutterstock), 73 (gpointstudio/iStockphoto), 74 a (Matthew Richardson/Alamy), 74 b (Jose Elias/Lusoimages – Technology/Alamy), 74 c (Shutterstock), 78 (kali9/iStockphoto), 79 cr (Shutterstock), 79 br (Shutterstock), 80 (Cary Wolinsky/National Geographic Image Collection), 82 tl (Shutterstock), 85 (Cheryl Zook/National Geographic), 85 bl (Mim Friday/Alamy), 86 (James Bedford/National Geographic Image Collection), 88 (Oliver Uberti/National Geographic Image Collection), 89 (Stockbyte/Getty Images), 90 (Jeff Gilbert/Alamy), 92 (Gosiek-B/iStockphoto), 94 1 (Elise Amendola/AP/Press Association Images), 94 2 (David Cheskin/PA Wire/Press Association Images), 94 3 (Keystone Pictures USA/Alamy), 94 4 (Robert I.M. Campbell/National Geographic Image Collection), 94 5 (Khalil Senosi/AP/Press Association Images), 95 (Herbert G. Ponting/National Geographic Image Collection), 96 (Robert Sisson/National Geographic Image Collection), 97 (aqualandphotography/iStockphoto), 97 (Shutterstock).

Illustrations by: Matthew Hams pp 77, 93; Kevin Hopgood pp 13, 57, 62 (pukao), 69, 81, 85; Oxford Designers & Illustrators p 22; David Russell pp 55, 56, 62, 72; Gary Wing pp 44, 67, 75, 99.

Printed in China by RR Donnelley
2 3 4 5 6 7 8 9 10 – 17 16 15 14 13

Contents

Unit 1 Colour

1a Red alert!

Listening hair colour

1 Which of these hair colours is not natural?

> black   blonde   brown   grey   purple   red
> white

2 🔊 **1.1** Listen to a radio clip from a 'pop science' programme. Are the sentences true (T) or false (F)?

1   Not many people buy hair dye in the United States.

2   In Scotland, two per cent of the population are natural redheads.

3   The gene for red hair also gives the body other benefits.

4   You can get red hair if both your parents carry the gene.

5   There are more redheads in the world now than before.

Glossary
dye (n) /daɪ/ a synthetic or natural substance used to change the colour of something
roots (n) /ruːts/ your origins, the place or group of people you come from

3 🔊 **1.1** Complete the sentences with the present simple or present continuous form of the verbs. Then listen again and check.

1   People _____ (spend) over a hundred million dollars every year on red hair dye.

2   It _____ (seem) that a lot of us _____ (like) red.

3   Natural redheads aren't very common – they _____ (belong) to a minority.

4   In Scotland two out of five people _____ (possess) the gene for red hair.

5   Some redheads _____ (feel) the cold more.

6   You _____ (need) two copies of the gene to get red hair.

7   That's why natural redheads _____ (disappear).

8   Young people often _____ (move) away from their home areas to work or to study.

9   The chances of someone meeting another person with the red-hair gene _____ (get) smaller.

10   Now some scientists _____ (speculate) that by the year 2100 true redheads will be extinct.

4 Look at the sentences in Exercise 3. Find words with the opposite meaning to these words.

1   artificial: _____

2   rare: _____

3   majority: _____

4   the heat: _____

5   greater: _____

Grammar present simple and present continuous

5 Read the article about dyes. Complete the article with the present simple and present continuous form of these verbs.

become	cause	come	contain	increase
know	not / understand	now / report	use	

W e [1] _____ dyes to change the colour of or add colour to many things. Textiles, cosmetics, food and drink products usually all [2] _____ food dyes. Some dyes [3] _____ from natural sources and others are synthetic. However, doctors [4] _____ that the number of people with allergic reactions to dyes [5] _____ . We [6] _____ that in a number of people some natural dyes [7] _____ rashes or respiratory problems. However, we [8] _____ why this reaction [9] _____ more common.

Grammar stative verbs

6 Read the comments by shoppers in a shopping centre. Complete the comments with the present simple and present continuous form of the verbs.

1 _____ you _____ (like) this colour? _____ it _____ (look) natural?
2 I _____ (look) for a shirt like this, but in a different size.
3 Excuse me. _____ this bag _____ (belong) to you?
4 What _____ it _____ (taste) like?
5 _____ you _____ (think) about buying this? It's very expensive.
6 I _____ (suppose) it's time to go home.

Vocabulary time expressions

7 Write sentences about Jamie. Use the present simple or present continuous and put the time expression in the correct position.

1 go out with friends / at weekends

2 spend time with his family / today

3 make lunch / at the moment

4 make lunch / usually

5 do housework / every day

6 do DIY / never

1b What colour is Tuesday?

Reading synesthesia

1 Read about Mark and answer the questions.

1 Is synesthesia an illness?

2 What happens when people have synesthesia?

3 Does it affect Mark's life at all?

4 How is Mark's synesthesia different from Kandinsky's?

5 What's the most frequent example of synesthesia?

6 Which part of the body is involved in synesthesia?

2 Underline words in the text connected to the senses. Decide if they are nouns or verbs. Then use some of the words to complete these sentences.

1 I don't like the _____ of bananas.
2 When my cat _____ a bird singing, it gets very excited.
3 Most people's _____ gets worse as they get older.
4 Our sense of _____ is most sensitive in our fingertips.
5 Animal noses have a highly developed sense of _____, compared with humans.

What **colour** is **Tuesday?**

My name is Mark. I'm Canadian and I have synesthesia. It's not a disease (although I think it sounds like one) and it doesn't really have any serious effects on my day-to-day life, but it is a strange condition. Synesthesia happens when two or more of your senses get mixed up. So in my case, for example, I taste words. My sense of taste works even when I'm not eating anything, but when I hear or read certain words. For me, the word 'box' tastes of eggs. That's just one example, of course. I'm reading one of the Sherlock Holmes stories at the moment and 'Sherlock' is another 'egg' word! It's a bit too much sometimes.

There are quite a few famous people with synesthesia: artists like David Hockney and Kandinsky, and musicians like Stevie Wonder and Liszt. Unfortunately for me I only share my synesthesia with them, not any great artistic skills. I read that Kandinsky's synesthesia mixed colour, hearing, touch and smell. To be honest, I don't think I'd like that. It seems very complicated.

My sister is synesthetic too and she sees words in colour. So when she sees the word 'Tuesday' or just thinks of the word 'Tuesday', she gets the feeling of 'brown'. Actually that kind of synesthesia, where the days of the week are coloured, is the most common type. I read somewhere that synesthesia is connected to the way our brains develop language and that there's a link between sounds and shapes. I don't understand the idea very well, but it sounds fascinating.

Grammar questions

3 Write the missing word in each question. Then write the answers.

1 Where Mark come from?

2 else in his family has the same condition?

3 What the name of his condition?

4 sense gives Mark problems?

5 What Stevie Wonder famous for?

6 What colour Mark's sister associate with *Tuesday*?

4 Dictation questions

1.2 Listen and write the questions. Then complete the answers for yourself and find out if you have synesthesia.

1
YOU:

2
YOU:

3
YOU:

4
YOU:

5 Pronunciation questions

a 1.2 Listen to the questions in Exercise 4 again. Draw the correct arrow above each question. Then practise the questions.

b Read the statements. Use these words to write follow-up questions. You can write more than one question for each statement.

Can you ... ?	What are ... ?
Do you ... ?	Where are ... ?
How many ... ?	Why do ... ?

1 This is a photo of one of my brothers.

2 I work in marketing.

3 We go to France every year.

4 I like to go home for the holidays.

5 I want to learn Japanese after English.

6 I love detective stories. I read for at least three hours every day!

Vocabulary feelings and personal states

6 Complete the sentences with these words.

| knowledge   luck   mourning   passion power |

1 Good _____ in your new job!
2 Are there any general _____ questions in this quiz?
3 I have no _____ to do anything. I'm not the boss.
4 The authorities announced two days of official _____ .
5 My friend has a _____ for food. She's always looking for new recipes.

7 Match and write the words with the comments.

| courage   happiness   love   sadness   wisdom |

1 _____
'That's Sunday morning when I know I can get up late.'

2 _____
'When I talk to my boss. He's so scary!'

3 _____
'What I get from my family every day.'

4 _____
'In the advice my grandparents give me.'

5 _____
'When I read about some people's difficult lives.'

1c A sense of colour

Listening colour blindness

1 Look at the two images. What number can you see in Image 1?

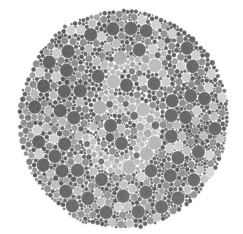

Image 1

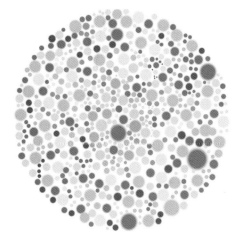

Image 2

These two images are similar to the ones opticians use to test if someone is colour-blind. People with normal colour vision see a number (as in Image 1). Colour-blind people can't see the number (Image 2).

2 🔊 **1.3** You are going to listen to an interview with someone who is colour-blind. First, choose the option you think is correct. Then listen and check.

1 Most colour-blind people can't tell the difference between red and *blue / green*.

2 Colour blindness is more common in *men / women*.

3 Our eyes have *two / three* types of cell that see colour.

4 Most colour-blind people *lead / can't lead* a normal life.

3 🔊 **1.3** Listen again. Answer the questions.

1 What percentage of men have colour blindness?

2 What problem does Holly have with her DVD player?

3 What colour is better for indicators on electrical goods?

4 What are the three colours the cells in our eyes can see?

5 What kind of jobs are not open to colour-blind people?

Word focus *see*

4 Look at two different meanings of the verb *see* from the interview. Then match the sentences with *see* (1–8) with the uses (a–h).

One kind of cell sees red. = 'the sense of sight'

Yes, of course, I see. = 'showing understanding'

1 I see better with my glasses.
2 Can you sit down? I can't see the screen.
3 As I see it, that's the best idea.
4 Do you see what I mean?
5 'You have to switch it on here.' 'Oh, I see.'
6 I see that Janet is leaving the company.
7 Come and see us this weekend.
8 Are you seeing anyone special at the moment?

a checking understanding
b giving news
c giving your opinion
d showing understanding
e the sense of sight
f to be in a relationship
g visibility of something
h visit someone

5 Replace four expressions in these exchanges with the correct form of *see*.

1 A: Louisa is going out with someone new.
  B: That's nice for her! Who is he?

2 A: I don't think I can help you.
  B: I understand. Well, thanks anyway.

3 A: I'm getting a lot of headaches.
  B: You need to go to a doctor.

4 A: Do you understand how easy it is?
  B: Oh yes. Thanks.

1d First impressions

Real life opening and closing conversations

1 Put the words in order to make statements and questions. Then write O for ways of opening conversations and C for ways of closing conversations.

1 a / you / pleasure / to / it's / meet

_____ .

2 don't / card / give / why / my / I / you

_____ ?

3 myself / may / introduce / I

_____ ?

4 stay / touch / in / let's

_____ .

5 you / to / talking / good / been / it's

_____ .

6 you / to / very / I'm / meet / pleased

_____ .

2 Complete this conversation with four of the sentences from Exercise 1.

W: Good morning! ¹ _____
I'm Will Marr.
G: How do you do? My name's Grace Larsen.
W: ² _____ ,
Grace. Are you a colleague of Daniel's?
G: Yes, I am, actually. We're both working on this project.
[…]
W: Well, Grace, ³ _____
I'm very interested in your ideas.
G: Thanks. ⁴ _____
You can reach me on both those two numbers.
W: OK, thanks.

3 Complete these ways of talking about what you do with prepositions.

1 I work _____ a design company.
2 I mostly work _____ special projects.
3 I'm an administrator _____ Brown's Bank.
4 I'm _____ Customer Services.
5 I'm looking _____ a new job at the moment.
6 I'm a student _____ City College.

4 Pronunciation short questions

a Match the comments (1–6) with the questions (a–f) to make short exchanges.

1 I'm a colleague of Daniel's.   a Can you?
2 She is one of our best customers. b Do you?
3 I work in our main office.   c Have you?
4 We've got a branch in your area.   d Is she?
5 It's one of our biggest shops.   e Are you?
6 I can call you tomorrow.   f Oh, is it?

b **1.4** Now listen to the exchanges. Tick (✓) the questions where the speaker sounds interested.

c **1.5** Listen to the comments again. Reply to each comment with a question. Sound interested in each case.

5 Grammar extra auxiliary verbs in short questions and answers

▶ **AUXILIARY VERBS IN SHORT QUESTIONS AND ANSWERS**

We use auxiliary verbs to make short questions and short answers. The auxiliary verbs are *be, have, do* and modal verbs. (*Be, have* and *do* can also be main verbs.)

Auxiliary verbs	Examples
be (am, are, is) *have (have, has)* modal verb (*can, must,* etc.) present simple (*do, does*) present continuous (*am, is, are*)	*Are you? Yes, I am.* *Has it? No, it hasn't.* *Can she? No, she can't.* *Do you? Yes, I do.* *Are they? Yes, they are.*

Write short questions or short answers in response to these comments.

1 I'm learning Greek at the moment.

_____

2 This paint is selling very well.

_____

3 Have you got my telephone number?
Yes, _____

4 Do you think you can win?
Yes, _____

5 Can you see what's happening?
No, _____

6 My colleagues are excited about this.

6 Listen and respond meeting people for the first time

1.6 Listen to comments from conversations where people meet for the first time. Respond with your own words. Then compare your response with the model answer that follows.

1 *Hello, how are you? My name's Grace Larsen.*

I'm very pleased to meet you. I'm Alberto Costa.

1e About us

Writing a profile

1 Writing skill criteria for writing: text type, style, reader, purpose and structure

a Read the extracts from company communications. Choose the correct option.

1 text type: *letter / website*

> I'm pleased to inform you that we are offering a new range of services.

2 style: *formal / informal*

> **Check out our new range!**
> **We think it's really cool!**

3 reader: *known / not known*

> Please note the following changes to your account.

4 purpose: *to give information / to advertise a product*

> Our clients are national and international companies.

b Read the information from a company profile. Match the sentences (a–d) with the headings (1–3). There are two sentences with one of the headings. Then use numbers with the headings to organise the information in a logical way.

Intersect Design

1 About our work | 2 Satisfied customers | 3 About us

ⓐ 'We always get fantastic results when we use Intersect.' *Blacks International*

ⓑ As well as this, we are working with a mobile phone operator on a new campaign. We work in all areas of advertising.

ⓒ At the moment, we are developing a new logo for a national radio station.

ⓓ We are a design agency with twenty years' experience.

2 Rewrite the sentences using the words in brackets in the correct position. There is sometimes more than one possibility.

1 I am working on a new product. (this year)

2 I can help you with new projects. (also)

3 We are advising a national company. (currently)

4 We are completing a major contract. (at this time)

5 We have offices in all main cities. (in addition to this)

6 We work in TV. (too)

3 Checking accuracy

Find and correct ten spelling mistakes in this profile.

1
2
3
4
5
6
7
8
9
10

> I am a freelance designar in the fashion industry. I also work as a consultent to a sportswear manufacturer. My especial areas of interest include working with natural textiles and dies. I am currently developping a range of baby clothes which are non-alergic.
>
> Outside of work, I have a pasion for abstract art, especially the colourfull works of Kandinsky. I am continualy trying to improve my own skills as a paintor.

Glossary
freelance (adj) /ˈfriːlɑːns/ doing work for different organisations rather than working all the time for one

Wordbuilding noun and verb → noun

> ▶ **WORDBUILDING noun and verb → noun**
>
> We can change the ending of some nouns and verbs to make words that describe what people do.
> *anthropology → anthropologist*
> *win → winner*

1 Complete the words in the table.

Noun/Verb	Suffix	Noun
anthropology art biology science	*-ist*	*anthropologist* ....
win administrate compete	*-er/-or*	*winner* ....
contest assist consult participate	*-ant*	*contestant* ....
optics electricity library music politics	*-ian*	*optician* ....

2 These verbs all take the same suffix. Which one?

> design   learn   manage   photograph
> research   speak   teach   train

3 Complete the sentences with nouns (singular or plural) from Exercises 1 and 2.

1   A .... helps you find books to borrow.

2   David Hockney is one of my favourite ....

3   Questionnaire for seminar .... : Please give us your views!

4   My new glasses are ready for me at the .... 's.

5   This is a great black and white image by a local ....

6   My friend's an .... He can fix your lights for you.

Learning skills study routines

> Learning English is easier and you are more successful when you follow a routine.

4 Draw a table showing your waking hours for each day of the week. Write your activities under the times. Then choose two colours and block off times:
- when you are free to study
- when you can study at the same time as you do something else, e.g. read on the train

	7 a.m.	8 a.m.	9 a.m.	10 a.m.	11 a.m.
Monday	coffee	train	work		break

5 How long do these activities need? Write 5, 30 or 60 (minutes) next to each one.
- reviewing vocabulary
- listening
- reading a magazine or graded reader
- doing Workbook exercises
- doing interactive (CD-ROM/online) exercises
- watching a DVD
- doing homework for class

6 Match activities from Exercise 5 with colour-blocked times in your table from Exercise 4.

7 Use your table to work out a realistic study routine.

Check!

8 Fill in the spaces (1–6) with places from Student's Book Unit 1 and find another place.

1   Orange means 'happiness' in this country.

2   There's a traditional prayer for peace here.

3   Van Gogh painted 'Yellow House' here.

4   The city that Hertz rental cars and the first yellow cabs come from.

5   Blue can be a sad colour in this country.

6   One of the South American countries where the Quechua people live.

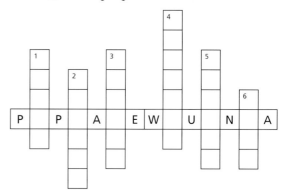

Unit 2 Performance

2a Street life

Reading La Rambla

1 Read what people say about La Rambla, a famous street in Barcelona. Write the names of the people.

1 Everything is new and exciting to ....
2 .... likes the reaction he gets from people on La Rambla.
3 Living on La Rambla has had a positive effect on .... 's art.
4 .... has been there for a long time.
5 .... likes the variety of La Rambla.

2 Read what people say again. Are the sentences true (T) or false (F)? Or is there not enough information (N) in the text?

1 La Rambla attracts entertainers from around the world.
2 The performances are free to the public.
3 There is always some kind of performance happening on La Rambla.
4 It's impossible to sleep if you live near La Rambla.

66 This place is full of life, every hour of every day. I've felt much more alive since I came here. It's really inspiring. My paintings have got so much more adventurous here. You can go out at night and always find something to do. I've never seen La Rambla without people. The place never sleeps. 99

Theo, portrait painter. Originally from Amsterdam.

66 I've just arrived and I've already heard about twenty different languages! It's awesome! There's so much going on. Everywhere you look there's some kind of performance. I especially like the puppeteers I saw this morning. I've never experienced anything like that before. 99

Kristen, language student. Originally from Chicago.

66 There is something very special about Barcelona and especially La Rambla. Every time you leave the house and go onto the street, you find some friends. It's more than a street and it's more than simply performing. It's a way of life. I've known the other performers for a long time now – they're like family. We help each other out. 99

Carmen, 'living statue'. Originally from Colombia.

66 We've been here for a few months. We adore this street. There's entertainment on every corner. And when we play and maybe ten people start dancing – it's beautiful. It's a great place. 99

Alvaro, musician. Originally from Angola.

66 I haven't lived here long enough yet to really understand it. But it's a fantastic mixture. Even the flower stalls are like art installations. You can see, I don't know, theatre, jugglers, acrobats, living statues, tango dancers from Argentina, musicians from Africa … performers from all around the world. 99

Tara, singer. Originally from London.

3 Find words for these performers in the text.

1 ....

3 ....

2 ....

4 ....

Grammar present perfect simple

4 Underline the present perfect simple verbs in the text about La Rambla. How many are there?

5 Complete the sentences with the present perfect form of the verbs and *for* or *since* where necessary.

1 We .... (be) here .... a few weeks and we love everything we .... (see) so far.

2 I .... (perform) every night .... I got here and the crowds are great.

3 We .... (never / have) so much success before.

4 My friend .... (live) here .... a couple of months and now I .... (decide) to join her.

5 I .... (always / want) to sing in public and now I can. I came here, I .... (become) more confident.

6 I .... (not / hear) this music before. It's quite unusual.

6 Rewrite the sentences adding *already, just* or *yet*.

1 Have you seen *Billy Elliot*?
....

2 Don't reserve me a ticket. I've bought mine.
....

3 I can't meet you later. I haven't finished my work.
....

4 We've been to see Lady Gaga. Wow!
....

5 I arrived this morning and I've seen dozens of performances.
....

6 I'm not sure what that means! I've started learning Spanish.
....

7 Pronunciation weak forms

🔊 **1.7** Listen and practise the sentences from Exercise 6.

Vocabulary musical styles

8 Write one of these words for each sentence.

catchy   cheerful   lively   melancholy
melodic   moving   repetitive   rhythmic
tuneless   unusual

1 This music has an interesting and pleasant tune.
....

2 It's different from anything you've ever heard before.
....

3 It's good for dancing to.
....

4 You can't stop singing it once you've heard it.
....

5 It's a little bit sad.
....

6 It's not really pleasant to listen to.
....

7 Every song sounds the same to me.
....

2b One of a kind

Grammar verb patterns: *-ing* form and *to* + infinitive

1 Complete the sentences with these words.

I agreed	I keep	My schedule
I finished	I need	We decided
I hope	I really enjoy	

1 _____ teaching my students to sing.
2 _____ to teach music when I leave college.
3 _____ making mistakes when I dance.
4 _____ to make more progress with my performance.
5 _____ involves getting up early every day.
6 _____ to involve the audience in our performance.
7 _____ taking classes last year.
8 _____ to take a role in the play.

2 Match the questions (a–b) with the sentences (1–9). Then complete the questions and sentences with the correct form of the verbs in brackets.

a I'm thinking about _____ (go) to the circus next week. Do you want _____ (come)?
b What have you decided _____ (do) for your birthday?

1 I intend _____ (take) it easy this year.
2 I think it's too late _____ (get) tickets.
3 I'm hoping _____ (go) to the theatre.
4 I'm not sure. I keep _____ (change) my mind.
5 No, thanks. I don't enjoy _____ (watch) animals perform.
6 Nothing special. I'm no good at _____ (plan).
7 Nothing yet. But my friends have promised _____ (not / give) me a surprise party.
8 OK, why not? I need _____ (do) something different.
9 _____ (see) animals doing tricks isn't my idea of entertainment.

3 Grammar extra *remember*, *stop* and *try*

> ► **REMEMBER, STOP and TRY**
>
> Both the *-ing* form and *to* + infinitive can follow these verbs, but there is a change in meaning.
>
> *stop* + *-ing* refers to the **activity** which stops:
> I only **stop practising** when the studio closes.
>
> *stop* + *to* + infinitive *refers to the* **reason** for stopping:
> I usually **stop to rest** when I'm tired.

Complete the sentences with the *-ing* form and *to* + infinitive form of the verbs.

1 When I'm tired, I stop _____ (dance).
2 If a new student comes in, we stop _____ (introduce) ourselves.
3 I usually remember _____ (change) my clothes before I paint.
4 I remember _____ (learn) the waltz with my father years ago.
5 I'm trying _____ (find) a way of keeping in touch with old friends.
6 I've tried _____ (join) Facebook, but most of my friends don't use it.

Listening man on a wire

4 🔊 **1.8** Listen to two friends, Robin and Judy, talking about this photo. Are the sentences true (T) or false (F)?

1 Judy doesn't like circuses.
2 Philippe Petit climbed up the outside of the World Trade Centre.
3 The photo makes Robin feel nervous.
4 Petit has walked between towers in several countries.
5 It took Petit six years to organise the World Trade Centre performance.

5 🔊 **1.8** Listen again. Complete the sentences.

1 I wonder why he wanted _____ that?
2 I can't imagine _____ on a wire.
3 He was lucky not _____ off.
4 He started in Paris in 1971 and then he kept _____ .
5 He decided _____ it in 1968.
6 _____ everything took six years.
7 And when people noticed him, he started _____ .

6 Complete the sentences with these words.

cheer up	cry	cry	laugh	laughing	sad
smile	smile	smile			

1 Don't _____ . It's only a film.

2 Come on! _____ for the camera!

3 _____ ! It's not the end of the world.

4 The situation was so absurd we didn't know whether to _____ or _____ .

5 It's great to hear you _____ for a change. You've seemed a bit _____ recently.

6 Have you noticed? When you _____ at people, they _____ back.

Vocabulary emotions

7 Vocabulary extra performing

a Write these verbs with the nouns.

give	make	play	sing	star	tell	write

1 _____ an instrument

2 _____ a joke

3 _____ a speech

4 _____ karaoke

5 _____ an album

6 _____ a play

7 _____ in a film

b Write sentences with expressions from Exercise 7a.

~~actors~~	authors	comedians	musicians
ordinary people	politicians	rock bands	

Example:
Actors star in films.

1 _____

2 _____

3 _____

4 _____

5 _____

6 _____

8 Dictation performing

1.9 Listen and write the sentences. Then decide if they are true for you.

1 _____

2 _____

3 _____

4 _____

5 _____

6 _____

'When I see three oranges, I juggle;
when I see two towers, I walk.'

Philippe Petit, High-wire artist, 1974

2c Life in a day

Listening a film review

1 💿 **1.10** Listen to a review of the film *Life in a day*. Answer the questions.

1 Why is the film called *Life in a day*?

2 What kind of film is it?

3 Who filmed it?

4 Are there any big stars in it?

5 Whose idea was it?

6 Where can you see it?

Glossary
footage (n) /ˈfʊtɪdʒ/ sequence of images on film
shot (v) /ʃɒt/ past participle of *shoot*: to record on film

2 💿 **1.10** Listen again. Write the information.

1 the date of the film

2 the length of the film

3 the number of cameras

4 the number of countries that received cameras

5 the hours of footage

6 the number of video clips

7 the number of countries that sent footage

3 What is the reviewer's opinion of the film? Choose one option (a–c).

a It's an unusual idea, but in the end it's a boring film.

b It's one of the best films she's ever seen.

c It's an interesting idea that has mainly succeeded.

Word focus *have*

4 Match the extracts (1–9) from the film review with the uses of *have* (a–e).

1 It has moments of drama.
2 Kevin Macdonald had an idea.
3 What have you got in your pocket?
4 Macdonald and his team had 4,500 hours of footage.
5 Macdonald didn't have a plan.
6 an English student having a drink …
7 market sellers in the Philippines having lunch …
8 The film has been pretty successful.
9 If you've missed it …

a an auxiliary verb (with the present perfect simple)
b an auxiliary verb (with *got*)
c a main verb (ownership or possession)
d a main verb (past tense, without *got*)
e a main verb (collocation with a noun)

5 Complete the sentences with the correct form of *have*. Use *got* where possible.

1 We _____ a great time last night.
2 Kevin Macdonald _____ made some great films.
3 _____ you _____ any of his films on DVD?
4 Let's _____ a drink after the show.
5 I _____ never been to Los Angeles.
6 Do you want to _____ lunch early today?
7 They're _____ a party after the film preview.
8 They _____ some problems with the cameras at first.

2d What's on?

Real life choosing an event

1 Complete each suggestion in two ways.

1 _____ see a film tonight?

2 _____ seeing a film tonight?

2 Respond to this suggestion in three ways.

'Let's go to the MegaScreen – the new Russell Crowe movie is on.'

_____

_____

_____

3 Write questions for these answers.

1 _____
There's a jazz concert at the City Hall.

2 _____
I think it's by Abi Morgan.

3 _____
It's got that guy who was in *Lost*.

4 _____
There's a late show at 11 p.m.

5 _____
It's the story of a young boy who loves dancing.

Vocabulary describing performances

4 Rewrite the sentences about performances as comments using these words. You can use the words in bold more than once.

absolutely awful boring brilliant
disappointing good hilarious **really** **very**

1 It was the funniest comedy show you've ever been to.
It was absolutely hilarious.

2 It was the worst concert you've ever been to.

3 You fell asleep during the play.

4 The exhibition was better than average.

5 You expected the performance to be better.

6 It was the best film you've ever seen.

5 Pronunciation intonation with *really*, *absolutely*, etc.

🎧 **1.11** Listen and repeat the sentences. Pay attention to your intonation.

6 Grammar extra adjectives ending in *-ed* and *-ing*

> ▶ **ADJECTIVES ENDING IN -ED and -ING**
>
> We use the present participle and past participle of some verbs as adjectives: *bore → bored → boring*
>
> -ed adjectives describe a person's state: *I'm bored. I was amazed.*
>
> -ing adjectives describe the characteristics of a thing or person: *It was boring. They were amazing.*

Complete the sentences with the *-ed* or *-ing* form of these verbs.

amaze bore depress disappoint fascinate
move

1 With so many choices, how can you say you're _____?

2 Those acrobats were _____. I don't know how they do that.

3 To be honest, I felt _____ by the lack of originality.

4 It's impossible not to be _____ by such beautiful music.

5 Another film about terrible childhoods? How _____!

6 What a _____ play that was! I'm still thinking about it now.

7 Listen and respond talking about events

🎧 **1.12** Listen to the questions. Respond with a comment. Use your own words. Then compare your response with the model answer that follows.

1
> *Do you fancy going to the theatre on Friday night?*

> *Yeah, why not?*

2e A portrait of an artist

Writing a profile

1 Writing skill linking ideas

a Read the sentences about the Indian musician Ravi Shankar. Cross out any options which are incorrect.

1 He started working with the Beatles in 1966, *so / therefore* he was instantly in the spotlight in the UK.

2 *Although / While* he's young in his mind, his body is too frail to play an instrument.

3 *Despite / In spite of* his age, he still enjoys music by artists such as Lady Gaga.

4 English music is written down. *In contrast, / For that reason,* Indian music is often improvised.

5 He appreciates most art forms, *but / so* he doesn't like electronic music.

b Rewrite the sentences with the words in brackets. Make any changes to verbs and punctuation as necessary.

a Even though he's from a classical Indian background, he's had mainstream success in the West. (despite)

....

....

b He played on Beatles records, so he quickly became well-known in Europe. (because of this)

....

....

c In spite of enjoying the music he made with the Beatles, he didn't like the attention it brought. (although)

....

....

d He loves Matisse and Picasso. Nevertheless, he doesn't believe in owning art. (while)

....

....

e He began as a dancer. However, he became more interested in making music. (but)

....

....

f In spite of not knowing much about classical Indian music, I love his work. (although)

....

....

2 Complete the sentences with the correct form of the verbs in brackets. Then decide which sentences (a–f) from Exercise 1b go in the boxes. Write the complete profile below.

1 Ravi Shankar is a classical Indian musician who .... (have) huge success over many decades.

2 I .... (follow) his work since I .... (see) him on TV a few years ago. ☐

3 This .... (begin) decades ago when he .... (work) with George Harrison, of the Beatles. ☐

4 Of course, I'm too young .... (remember) the Beatles.

5 I enjoy the music he .... (make) nowadays. ☐

6 I like it because it .... (sound) beautiful and unusual to me. It's really different from Western music.

7 There's so much different stuff out there .... (listen) to, and I enjoy it all.

Wordbuilding adjective + noun

> ▶ **WORDBUILDING adjective + noun**
>
> Some adjectives and nouns often go together.
> *outside world*   *popular culture*

1 Match the adjectives with the nouns. They are all in Student's Book or Workbook Unit 2. More than one combination is possible.

> **Adjectives**
> bad   big   English   famous   living   mainstream
> ordinary   romantic   special   traditional   young

> **Nouns**
> actor   comedies   couple   effects   influence   mood
> people   role   statue   student   success

2 Complete the sentences with adjective + noun combinations from Exercise 1.

1   The Beatles were a _____ on many pop groups.

2   The _____ in the flat next door are really friendly.

3   This band has been around for a couple of years but hasn't had _____ yet.

4   The actress Meg Ryan appeared in a lot of _____ early in her career.

5   My favourite films have amazing _____ that I can believe in.

6   If I'm in a _____, listening to music helps me feel more cheerful.

Learning skills mistakes

> Making mistakes is part of learning. Thinking about mistakes in different categories can help you.

3 Look at these types of mistakes. Try to write down an example of each kind of mistake.

- mistakes you make because you haven't learned the correct word or structure yet

- mistakes that are common to all learners with the same first language as you

- mistakes that you make when speaking because you haven't got enough time to think about what you say

- mistakes that are 'yours' – things you personally have problems with

- mistakes that mean people can't understand your message properly

4 Do you make mistakes with any of these things? Write an example.

1   the verb tense in sentences like *I haven't met many people since I moved here.*

2   the verb form in constructions like *Listening to music helps me feel more cheerful.*

3   adjectives like *bored/boring*

5 Keep a record of mistakes you make often. Think about what kind of mistake they are. Write down the correct language and try to remember it. But don't worry too much about the mistakes that don't affect how well people understand you. And don't worry if it takes a while to correct your mistakes.

Check!

6 Answer these questions. The first letter of each answer spells a word. What it is is?

1 A photo or painting of a person.	1	
2 Actors, comedians, acrobats, singers, etc. are all	2	
3 Music from Jamaica.	3	
4 A style of music and dance from southern Spain.	4	
5 A large group of people who play musical instruments together.	5	
6 The title of one of Baz Luhrmann's films.	6	
7 Someone who does clever tricks for an audience.	7	
8 Really, really bad.	8	
9 Joining a club is a good way of making ..... friends.	9	
10 A group of people who sing together.	10	
11 A kind of coffee.	11	

3a Underwater

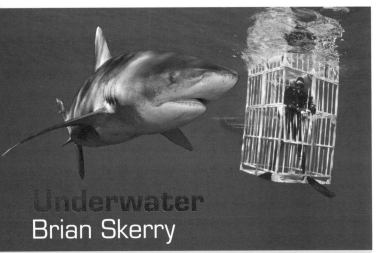

Underwater
Brian Skerry

1 Finding the oceanic whitetip shark is an experience I won't forget. This is one of the most dangerous sharks in the world, but its numbers are falling. They used to be common around the Bahamas, but most people say they haven't seen them for years. Just as we arrived there, some sports fishermen in the central Bahamas saw some oceanic whitetips when they were fishing for tuna. So I planned sixteen days to go searching for them.

For the first few days out of Palm Beach, we didn't see a thing. Then, on the fifth day, I was looking out from the bridge when I spotted a shark on the surface. The white tip of its dorsal fin was sticking out of the water, so I knew we had an oceanic whitetip. I quickly put on my wetsuit and jumped in the water. The shark was very curious about me and swam right up to me. It was about three metres long and it even stayed around while we were putting the cage in the water for the scientist. I got some great pictures! That was really the high point of the assignment.

2 At the end of the assignment, after a year of work, we were going after the great hammerhead shark. This species is so elusive that there were no pictures of it up until five or six years ago. For the entire first week, the weather was appalling and it was impossible to dive. It was very frustrating. Then, on the eighth day, my assistant had to fly home because his mother was seriously ill.

Suddenly, I was working alone as well as trying to deal with the bad weather. That was definitely the worst moment on the assignment. It is so important to have a really good assistant with you. Without him there, my workload more than doubled. While I was trying to decide what to do, the weather unexpectedly improved and I got a couple of not-bad days! And on one of those days, everything clicked and I got some great pictures of a hammerhead. I was lucky.

Reading on assignment

1 Read the interview with Brian Skerry about his year-long assignment photographing sharks. Write the number of the story (1–2) next to the heading. There is one extra heading.

a What was one of your worst experiences covering this story?
b What was one of your strangest experiences covering this story?
c What was one of your best experiences covering this story?

2 These statements are true for one or both of Skerry's stories. Write W (whitetip), H (hammerhead) and B (both).

1 The sharks were difficult to find.
2 Bad weather made it almost impossible to do any work.
3 Some fishermen told Skerry where the sharks were.
4 Skerry had to work without an assistant.
5 Skerry got into the water as soon as he saw a shark.
6 The shark spent some time swimming close to Skerry.
7 Skerry wasn't sure what to do.
8 Skerry was pleased with the photos he took.

3 Find these words and expressions in the text. Choose the correct option.

1 spotted: *photographed / saw*
2 high point: *best moment / top of the boat*
3 deal with: *survive / solve the problem*
4 workload: *amount of work you have to do / problems*
5 doubled: *increased by twice as much / increased by three times as much*
6 clicked: *was quiet / was successful*

Glossary
bridge (n) /brɪdʒ/ part of a boat or ship where the captain normally stands
dorsal fin (n) /ˈdɔːrsəl fɪn/ the part of a shark's back that sticks up
elusive (adj) /ˈɪlusɪv/ extremely rare and difficult to see
wetsuit (n) /ˈwetsuːt/ rubber clothes for water sports

Grammar past simple and past continuous

4 Write questions for these answers. Use the information from the interview.

1 When _____ ?
  When they were fishing for tuna.

2 When _____ ?
  While he was looking out from the bridge.

3 How _____ ?
  Because the white tip of its dorsal fin was sticking out of the water.

4 What _____ ?
  They were going after the great hammerhead shark.

5 What _____ ?
  Skerry's assistant flew home.

6 What _____ ?
  He was trying to decide what to do.

5 Complete the sentences with the correct form of the verbs in brackets.

1 We _____ a shark when we _____ . (see / surf)

2 I _____ back into the boat when I _____ my camera into the water. (climb / drop)

3 It _____ a beautiful morning. The sun _____ over the horizon and the fish _____ . (be / come up / jump)

4 It _____ to rain while we _____ a really good sequence. (start / film)

5 We _____ in the boat, quickly _____ our equipment and _____ home. (get / pack up /go)

6 While we _____ back to land, the wind suddenly _____ a lot stronger. (sail / get)

6 Pronunciation irregular past simple verbs

a 🔊 **1.13** Listen to the sentences and write the irregular past simple verbs.

1 _____
2 _____
3 _____
4 _____
5 _____
6 _____
7 _____
8 _____

b Which verbs have the same sound?

_____ and _____
_____ and _____

Vocabulary water and recreation

7 Write these words in the correct place.

canoeing   diving   fishing   jet-skiing
kayaking   rafting   rowing   parasailing
sailing   scuba diving   snorkelling   surfing
swimming   synchronised swimming   water polo
water-skiing   windsurfing

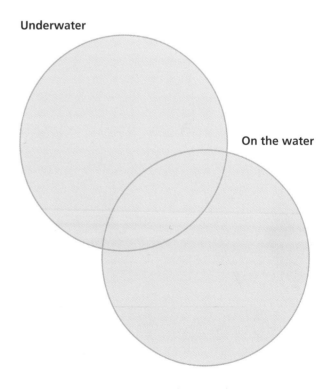

Underwater

On the water

3b Problems and rescues

Vocabulary at sea

1 Write the names of these things. They are all on Student's Book pages 36–37.

1 ....

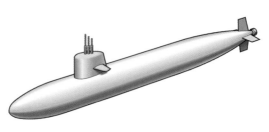

2 ....

3 ....

4 ....

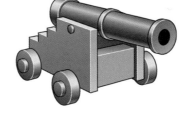

5 ....

6 ....

Listening Hurricane Mitch

2 What kind of landscape does the photo show? Choose one option (a–c).

  a desert
  b farmland
  c forest

3 🔊 **1.14** You are going to listen to the introduction to a programme about hurricanes. Tick (✓) the words you think you will hear. Then listen and check.

clouds	destructive	flooded	ocean
powerful	rainfall	sand	tornado	tropical
waves	wet	winds	

4 🔊 **1.14** Listen again and choose the correct option (a–c).

1 Hurricanes begin in the … .
   a Atlantic Ocean
   b Indian Ocean
   c Pacific Ocean

2 There is a hurricane season … .
   a every month
   b every year
   c every ten years

3 Hurricane Mitch affected … .
   a North and South America
   b the Caribbean and South America
   c the Caribbean and Central America

4 … fell in one day in Honduras.
   a Six days' rain
   b Two months' rain
   c Two hundred days' rain

5 What happened to these things during Hurricane Mitch? What was responsible: wind or water?

1 bridges

2 farmland

3 rivers

4 roads

5 sand

6 trees

Grammar past perfect simple

6 Change the verbs to the past perfect where necessary.

1 By the time the storm reached land, most residents left the area.

2 When people got back home, they were amazed at what happened.

3 In some places, before the hurricane there were trees, but now there was nothing.

4 Many roads and bridges disappeared by the end of the first day.

5 After the hurricane, there was a desert where people had farms.

6 It became clear how much changed when people saw the satellite images.

7 Complete the news item with the past simple and past perfect simple form of these verbs.

| be | become | can | already / die | manage |
| try | | | | |

Rescuers in Scotland ¹_____ to return twenty whales to the sea this weekend. The whales ²_____ from a larger group that ³_____ stuck on the beach. Several other whales ⁴_____ before the rescuers ⁵_____ to help them. Earlier the rescue team ⁶_____ unsuccessfully to stop the whales from coming too close to the shore. The reason for the whales' behaviour is not clear.

8 Dictation a rescue

🔊 **1.15** Listen and write the information from a news item about Coast Guards. When you hear 'full stop', this means you have reached the end of a sentence. Then put the sentences in order.

a

b

c

d

e

3c Bottled water

Listening water on tap?

WHO DRINKS THE MOST BOTTLED WATER?

Top ten markets by litres per person in 2006			
203	Italy	129	Germany
197	United Arab Emirates	126	Spain
191	Mexico	117	Lebanon
149	France	110	Switzerland
145	Belgium/Luxembourg	104	United States

1 Look at the information about bottled water. Where do people drink the most bottled water?

2 🔘 **1.16** Listen to part of a radio programme about Bundanoon, a bottled water free town in Australia. Answer the questions.

  1 Where does Bundanoon get its water from?

  2 What did the water company want to do?

  3 What had local businessman Huw Kingston done?

  4 What happened at the town meeting?

  5 When did environmental groups start to support the town?

3 🔘 **1.16** Listen again and complete the sentences.

  1 The residents of Bundanoon were against the water company's plans because _____ .

  2 Huw Kingston wanted the town to _____ and _____ .

  3 A few residents heard about another Australian town that _____ .

  4 The residents discovered that the carbon footprint of bottled water _____ .

  5 If a visitor to Bundanoon wants some water, _____ .

Glossary
ban (v) /bæn/ prohibit
pioneer (n) /ˌpaɪəˈnɪə/ the first to do something
reusable (adj) /ˌriːˈjuːzəbl/ can be used more than once

Word focus *get*

4 Look at these sentences from the radio programme. Replace the words in bold with four of these words. There is one extra word.

become   entered   met   obtain   received

  1 And how did you **get** involved in the story?

  2 A few residents **got together** to investigate how we could go 'bottled water free'.

  3 After they wrote about us, we **got** a lot of support from environmental movements.

  4 All the water in our town is free, so you can **get** it from the tap.

5 Match the comments (1–6) with the responses (a–f).

  1 How did you get on at the meeting?
  2 This company wants to bottle the town's water.
  3 Can you get me a paper when you go to the shop?
  4 How's the campaign going?
  5 How did you get your picture in the papers?
  6 What a crazy week!

  a We just got in touch with the journalists about the campaign.
  b I don't get it. Why do they want to do that?
  c I know! I can't wait for things to get back to normal.
  d Really well. They agreed to all of our suggestions.
  e Things are getting better now that we've been on TV.
  f Yes, sure.

3d No way!

Real life telling stories

1 Complete the story with these words.

after	during	later	suddenly	then	while

Did I ever tell you about the time I went fishing with my girlfriend's father? ¹ _____ the drive to the lake, he told me about all the huge fish he'd caught. ² _____ half an hour of this, I wanted to go home. Anyway, we'd been on the lake for a couple of hours when ³ _____ , my fishing rod started to move. ⁴ _____ I was trying to bring the fish in, he was shouting, 'It's massive, really big!' Thirty minutes ⁵ _____ , I still hadn't managed to get the fish in the boat. And ⁶ _____ I dropped my rod in the water. My girlfriend's father was horrified. He never spoke to me again.

2 Grammar extra *when/while/as*

> ▶ *WHEN/WHILE/AS*
>
> We can use *when, while* and *as* to show that two actions happened *at the same time.*
>
> Use *when* with a short action (past simple) which happened during a longer action:
> *We were sitting in the boat when my fishing rod moved.*
>
> Use *while* for two longer actions:
> *While I was trying to control it, he was shouting.*
>
> Use *as* for two short actions:
> *As I stepped forwards, I dropped the rod.*

Circle the best option.

1 We were driving to the river *while / when* we ran out of petrol.

2 *As / While* I got out of the car, I felt the rain.

3 *While / When* we were putting petrol in the car, the sky was getting darker.

4 *As / When* I walked to the till, I decided to go home.

5 We were talking about our plans *while / when* my phone rang.

6 *As / While* I got back home, the sun came out.

3 Pronunciation *was* and *were*

a 🎧 **1.17** Listen and repeat the sentences you hear. Pay attention to how you say *was* and *were*.

b Now practise saying sentences 1, 3 and 5 from Exercise 2.

4 Listen and respond asking about things that happened

🎧 **1.18** Listen to people talking about things that happened to them. Respond with a question. Use your own words. Then compare your response with the model answer that follows.

1
> *Did I ever tell you about the time we ran out of petrol?*

> *No. Where were you going?*

3e What a weekend!

Writing a blog post

1 Jenna's computer has made a mess of her blog. Put the text in the correct order. Write numbers next to the lines.

Titanic Fanatics trip to Belfast

Well, that certainly was a weekend to remember! After months of
embarking on a new life. The entire experience was
<u>here</u>.
members of the *Titanic Fanatics society*, and we unexpectedly
especially moving as I thought about all those heroic passengers
On Saturday morning we made our way to the spectacular
completely packed, of course – nobody wanted to miss the centenary
planning, we finally made it to Belfast to see where the whole
bumped into some familiar faces on Friday evening too. The hotel was
Wandering slowly through the authentically recreated cabins was
Titanic Belfast centre. It was thrilling to see the place where
Titanic was designed, built and launched a century ago.
tragic *Titanic* story began. There were sixteen of us altogether, all
unforgettable and you can see all my photos and read more
weekend.

a _1_
b _____
c _____
d _____
e _____
f _____
g _____
h _____
i _____
j _____
k _____
l _____
m _____
n _____
o _____

2 Writing skill interesting language

a Match these words with the expressions Jenna used.

> amazing   arrived in   emotional   exciting
> full of people   met   some friends   sad   starting
> went

1 we finally **made it to** Belfast: _____
2 **tragic** story: _____
3 we **bumped into** some **familiar faces**: _____
4 **packed**: _____
5 we **made our way** to: _____
6 spectacular: _____
7 thrilling: _____
8 moving: _____
9 **embarking on** a new life: _____

b Complete the sentences with words from Exercise 2a.

1 The new aquatic sports building is _____ .
2 I _____ my boss at the cinema.
3 It was rush hour, so the bus was _____ .
4 I got on the train and _____ to my seat.
5 I was surprised to see _____ at the exhibition.
6 This young boy had a _____ life before going to America.

3 Look at the words. Find four words to describe:

1 a view: _____ , _____ , _____ , _____
2 an experience: _____ , _____ , _____ , _____
3 a place you are in: _____ , _____ , _____ , _____
4 ways of 'going': _____ , _____ , _____ , _____

impressive **packed**
exciting magnificent **travel**
crowded exhilarating **spectacular**
busy electrifying take off thrilling
full fabulous move on set off

4 Use these notes to write the second part of Jenna's blog.

- Saturday evening / got dressed up
- dinner / spectacular dining room
- whole thing / recreation / dinner on *Titanic*
- dining room / packed / thrilling / authentic costumes
- bumped into / people / earlier / joined
- food / amazing / whole thing / moving

Wordbuilding adverbs

> ▶ **WORDBUILDING adverbs**
>
> Most adverbs are formed by adding -ly to adjectives. Some adverbs and adjectives are the same.
> quick (adjective) → quickly (adverb)
> fast (adjective) = fast (adverb)

1 Make adverbs from these adjectives. The adverbs are all in Student's Book or Workbook Units 1–3.

> complete   definite   easy   extreme
> fast   fortunate   normal   quick
> serious   slow   unexpected
> unpleasant   unsuccessful

2 How many ways can you complete these sentences? Use adjectives or adverbs from Exercise 1.

1 The raft came down the river really … .

2 … , this doesn't happen often.

3 He's a rather … person.

4 We were … lost.

5 I made several … attempts and then gave up.

6 The hippo … turned towards us.

Learning skills keeping a journal

3 One of the most difficult things about learning English is remembering everything. Keeping a journal can help you. Look at the page from a journal and tick (✓) the things the student has included.
- diagrams/drawings
- example sentences
- grammar
- how he/she feels about something
- listening
- other students
- pictures
- questions for the teacher
- reading
- reminders to do things
- self-evaluation
- speaking
- test scores
- vocabulary
- writing

3 Nov	8/10 in a vocabulary test! ☺
6 Nov	
new words	shipwreck iceberg nearby edge
grammar	
reading	The reading text was difficult! Read it again at the weekend.
	Paola told me about going through the Channel tunnel – very funny.
sentence	I got back home at 11.30.
10 Nov	We watched a DVD about water in India.

4 Look at the things in the diary entry which are underlined. Why do you think the student has underlined them?

5 Choose the options which work best for you. Then try keeping a journal for a month.

1 type of journal: *notebook / computer-based / online blog*
2 entries: *every day / after every class / every week*
3 type of entry: *notes / a narrative / analytical*
4 focus: *what I learn / how I learn / strong points / weak points*
5 re-read: *after each entry / every week / every fortnight*

Check!

6 All these words go with *water*. Which ones are in the word square? Use the clues to help you.

> boiling   bottled   clean   cold   deep   dirty   fresh
> hot   rain   river   running   salt   sea   tap

X	F	L	H	H	N	I	E	K	O
H	R	I	R	U	N	N	I	N	G
A	E	B	S	E	L	A	Z	B	I
R	S	O	Q	V	O	B	U	O	T
E	H	I	P	N	H	O	T	Y	S
O	A	L	Z	I	P	T	E	W	A
R	A	I	N	P	L	T	I	R	L
P	L	N	I	E	U	L	T	T	T
E	B	G	S	U	A	E	N	B	O
Y	U	V	C	O	L	D	X	R	U

1 It falls from the sky and you can collect it in a tank.
2 Some people only drink this kind, but it's expensive.
3 Lakes are almost always this kind of water.
4 When your home gets a continuous supply from pipes.
5 If you're in this kind of water, it means you have done something wrong.
6 This kind is needed to make a cup of tea.
7 The oceans and seas of the world are made of this.
8 When you don't like an idea, you pour this kind of water on it.

Unit 4 Opportunities

4a Future world

Listening children of the future

1 💿 **1.19** Listen to four parents of young babies talking about their children's futures. Tick (✓) the things the speakers (1–4) mention. You can tick more than one thing for each speaker.

	1	2	3	4
education				
environment				
health				
home				
languages				
work				

2 💿 **1.19** Listen again to the predictions the parents make about these things. Are they sure (S) or not sure (NS) of their predictions?

1 using a computer
2 leaving school
3 using robots
4 driving electric cars
5 working full time
6 living to be 100
7 effects of climate change
8 speaking Chinese

Grammar predictions with *will*

3 Complete the predictions with one word so that they are 100 per cent sure. Sometimes more than one option is correct.

1 The world .... be a very different place in a few years' time. I'm sure of that.
2 He .... (not) leave school at 16 like I did.
3 Robots and computers .... take care of all the routine, boring things.
4 She .... won't work full-time.
5 They'll .... find cures for many of the health problems we face today.

4 Complete the predictions with one word so that they are NOT 100 per cent sure. Sometimes more than one option is correct.

1 She'll .... live to be a 100.
2 She .... get ill at some point in her life.
3 This .... affect their world in ways we haven't imagined.
4 They .... not learn it at school.
5 That .... be a challenge!

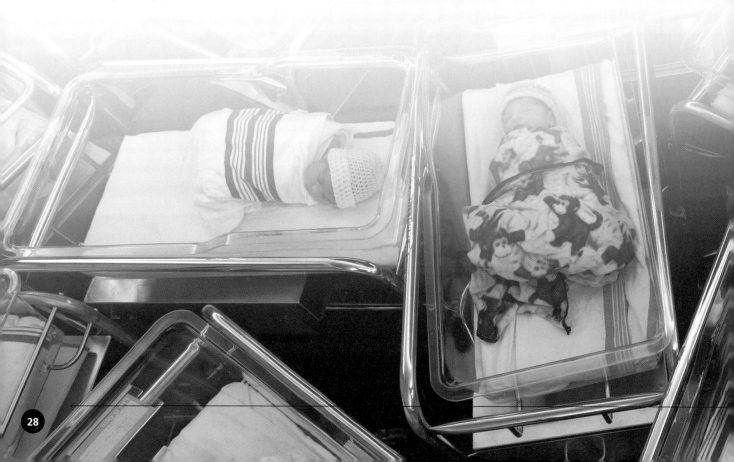

5 Read the first sentence. Then choose the logical prediction (a or b).

1 We're planning to have a baby.
   a It might be a girl.
   b It will be a girl.

2 My son has a cold.
   a He may get better soon.
   b He'll get better soon.

3 People are living longer these days.
   a I could live to be 100.
   b I'll live to be 100.

4 Electric cars are on sale now.
   a Some people might buy them.
   b Some people will buy them.

6 Dictation predictions

💿 **1.20** Listen and write the six predictions. Then decide how much you agree with each one. (✗ = disagree, ✓ = mostly agree, ✓ ✓ = completely agree)

1 ....
2 ....
3 ....
4 ....
5 ....
6 ....

Vocabulary jobs

7 Complete and rewrite the words that describe these jobs.

1 film star: xctng and glmrs

   .... , ...

2 fire fighter: dngrs and dmdng

   .... , ...

3 train driver: rspnsbl and rtn

   .... , ...

4 vet: rwdng and stsfyng

   .... , ...

8 Complete the sentences with the correct form of *job* or *work*.

1 The project will bring lots of new .... to the area.

2 Do you enjoy .... here?

3 How often do you take a day off ....?

4 How can you do three .... at once? That's impossible!

5 She's got a lot to do at .... at the moment.

6 What's your ....?

9 Read about Maria and decide what her job is.
   a an accountant
   b a manager
   c a technician

> Maria works for a large multinational company. Her hours are from 9 a.m. to 5 p.m., Monday to Friday. She uses a computer all day and is very good at maths. Her job is a bit routine, but it's secure and quite well-paid. She hopes to be promoted soon.

4b Now what?

Vocabulary education

1 Complete the questions with these expressions. Then answer the questions.

become an apprentice	leave school
drop out of college	pass an exam
get a degree	resit an exam
go to university	stay on at school

In your country:

1 At what age can you legally _____ ?

2 Do many teenagers _____ after compulsory education?

3 What is the minimum mark you need to _____ ?

4 How many times can you _____ after you fail it?

5 Do people _____ close to home or in other towns?

6 Is it easy to _____ in a factory?

7 How many years does it take to _____ ?

8 Do many people _____ and get a job instead?

Reading going back

2 Look at the photo of Lorna. Decide which option you think is correct in each question. Then read the email and check your ideas.

1 Is she in a bar or a café?

2 Is she a waitress or a chef?

3 Does she work there or is she the owner?

4 Is she in her twenties or her thirties?

5 Is she single or married?

3 Read Lorna's email again. Answer the questions.

1 Where is she from?

2 Where has she been for the past year?

3 Why is she writing to her brother?

4 What does she think about London?

4 Correct the factual mistakes in these sentences.

1 Lorna's brother is finishing his apprenticeship soon.

2 Lorna will be in Auckland next week.

3 She's going to look for a new job in London.

4 She's found somewhere to live in Auckland.

5 She won't be able to stay with Brett.

6 She promises to take her brother to Chelsea.

Hey little brother, how are you doing?

I bet you can't wait to leave school and start that apprenticeship. I can't remember if you got a place at Autofit or City Bridges …

Anyway, here's some news – I'm coming back after this job. Don't tell Mum yet – I want to surprise her. I'll be in Auckland in May or June, I think. The café I'm working in is losing customers and money, and two staff are leaving next week! I'll be next, I reckon. So I'm going to take a few months out and see what turns up back home. I could look for another job here, but after almost a year of waitressing I feel like doing something new. London has been brilliant, but I'm not going to stay here forever. I suppose I'll have to think about what I'm going to do in the long term at some point soon.

I'll need to find somewhere to live in Auckland, that's the first thing. I guess you're going to stay at home with Mum. Apprentices don't earn much, do they? I was talking to Brett and he's staying on next year to do another course at college, or something, so I might be able to stay with him while I do some job-hunting. If that doesn't work out … well, I'll think of something! I may even move back to live with you and Mum! But at 25, I don't think that's such a good idea.

Anyway, this is just to let you know my plans, as far as they go at the moment! See you in a couple of months – I'll bring you a Chelsea football shirt!

Lorna

xxxx

Word focus *do*

5 Find seven more examples of the verb *do* in the email. Write the expressions in the correct place.

do as an auxiliary verb

Example:

Dont't tell Mum yet

1 ....
2 ....
3 ....

do as a main verb

Example:

how are you doing?

4 ....
5 ....
6 ....
7 ....

6 Complete the sentences with these words.

chemistry	nothing
do you	pottery
hair and make-up	the shopping

1 How .... do? I'm Mr Erikson.
2 My sister's doing .... at university.
3 Are you going to do your own .... for the wedding?
4 I'll do .... tomorrow – it's too late to go now.
5 Sometimes the best solution is to do ....
6 I'm going to do a .... evening class with a friend.

Grammar future forms

7 Look at the uses of future forms (a–c) and the example. Then write sentences using the appropriate form as in the example.

a a plan or intention decided before the moment of speaking
b a decision made at the moment of speaking
c an arrangement to do something at a specified (or understood) time in the future

Example:

I / look for a new job (a)
I'm going to look for a new job.

1 I / start my new job next week (c)

2 I / meet you tonight (b)

3 we / move house soon (c)

4 my friend / leave college (a)

5 my friend / do an exam tomorrow (c)

6 I / help you study (b)

7 I / see you later (b)

8 Pronunciation *I'll*

🔊 **1.21** Listen to the sentences. Write the word which includes the letter *l*. Notice how you hear a short /u/ sound before the /l/. Repeat the sentences.

1 ....   4 ....
2 ....   5 ....
3 ....   6 ....

4c Looking ahead

Vocabulary pay and conditions

1 Choose the best option.

1   I'll see you at three. I can get off early because I'm on *flexi-time / overtime*.

2   It's hard to feel motivated when we haven't had a *bonus / pay rise* for seven years.

3   I love working in a clothes shop, especially because they give *staff discounts / pension schemes* on the products!

4   We sold more than we expected, so I think we'll all get a *bonus / pay rise* this month.

5   I'm working this Sunday – it's *flexi-time / overtime*, so the pay is good.

6   I won't be able to come travelling with you. I only get one week's *long hours / paid holiday* this year.

Listening radio interviews

2 🎵 **1.22** Choose the correct option (a–c). Then listen to part of a radio programme and check.

1   How 'old' is the world wide web?
  a   less than fifteen years old
  b   between twenty and thirty years old
  c   more than forty years old

2   What do we call the occasion when you are given your university degree?
  a   final meeting
  b   graduation ceremony
  c   leaving party

3   What do we call the occasion married couples celebrate every year?
  a   engagement party
  b   marriage ceremony
  c   wedding anniversary

3 🎵 **1.22** Listen again. Are the sentences true (T) or false (F)?

1   The presenter talks about last week's programme.
2   Anton doesn't want to settle down yet.
3   Anton's job pays well.
4   Carey is about to start university.
5   Carey isn't working at the moment.
6   Carey and Anton have both overcome challenges in their lives.

4 Answer the questions using information from the radio programme.

1   What is the 'Internet generation'?

2   What does Anton say about plans?

3   Why does Carey believe you need an open mind?

4   Why do you think the programme is called *Turning 21*?

5 Pronunciation *'ll*

a 🎵 **1.23** The contracted form of *will* (*'ll*) is not stressed. Listen to these pairs of sentences. Which sentence do you hear first?

1   a   We'll meet some of the 'Internet generation'.
  b   We meet some of the 'Internet generation'.

2   a   We'll find out what it means to be 21 today.
  b   We find out what it means to be 21 today.

3   a   We'll have my graduation ceremony.
  b   We have my graduation ceremony.

4   a   I'll try anything.
  b   I try anything.

b 🎵 **1.23** Listen again. Practise saying the sentences.

4d Would you mind ... ?

Vocabulary job requirements

1 Choose the best option.

1 Researchers need to be *creative / well-organised* as they deal with lots of information.

2 Entrepreneurs need to be *methodical / self-confident* to make their ideas succeed.

3 Farmers need to be *creative / independent* if they are self-employed.

4 Accountants need to be *energetic / methodical* because their work is very detailed.

5 Managers need to be *creative / well-organised* when trying to solve problems.

6 Technicians need to be *conscientious / self-confident* as their work can be routine.

2 Grammar extra predictions with *going to*

> ▶ **PREDICTIONS WITH *GOING TO***
>
> We can use *going to* to make a prediction based on something that means the speaker thinks it is certain to happen:
> *My company is in trouble. I'm going to lose my job.*

Match the situations (1–4) with the predictions (a–d).

1 I'm so nervous about this interview.

2 The interview was awful.

3 The other candidate was more experienced.

4 Your CV is really strong.

a They aren't going to offer me the job.

b She's going to get the job.

c You're going to get an interview.

d It's going to be a disaster.

Real life making and responding to requests

3 Use combinations of these words to complete the requests. You can use the words more than once.

| all right | be | can | could | do | if | is |
| it | mind | OK | to | will | would | you |

1 .... reading this letter for me?

2 .... I used your computer?

3 .... have a look at this application form?

4 .... give your name?

5 .... be able to help me tomorrow?

6 .... I borrow your phone?

4 Pronunciation weak and strong auxiliary verbs

💿 **1.24** Listen and repeat the exchanges you hear. Pay attention to the weak and strong auxiliary verbs.

5 Listen and respond answering questions

💿 **1.25** Listen to the questions about a job application process. Respond with your own answer. Then compare your response with the model answer that follows.

1

> Are you looking for a new job at the moment?

> Yes, I am actually.

4e I enclose my CV

Writing a covering letter

1 Writing skill formal style

a Which of these things (a–d) is not a feature of formal letters?

a concise sentences
b formal phrases to begin sentences
c contractions
d standard phrases to open and close the letter

b Rewrite the phrases and sentences in the appropriate style for a covering letter.

1 Hi Mr Brown,

2 I saw your advert.

3 Here's my application form.

4 I'm a fun kind of person.

5 I've done this kind of work before.

6 Do you want to interview me soon?

7 Send me an email or text me.

8 All the best,

2 Read the profile and the advert. Underline the sections in the advert that correspond to the profile information.

Profile: Manuel Santos

• enthusiastic

• hard-working

• enjoys working with people

Wants: a job in catering

Experience: restaurants, cafeterias (UK, Portugal)

Availability: now

AROMA CAFÉS

Home | About | Jobs

We are an expanding chain of specialist cafés looking for outgoing, energetic waiters/waitresses.

• part-time position leading to full-time opportunity

You will be responsible for

• serving customers
• maintaining the stocks
• maintaining a clean environment

Characteristics of ideal candidates are:

• some experience in catering or retail
• excellent communication skills
• hard-working and good under pressure
• authorised to work in the UK

Send application form and covering letter to:
Jim.Kapoor@aroma
Ref 119/XG Closing date 31 October

3 Write a covering email from Manual Santos to go with the completed application form for this job.

Wordbuilding phrasal verbs

> **▶ WORDBUILDING phrasal verbs**
>
> We often use phrasal verbs when talking about our actions.
> *drop out*
> *stay on*

1 Match the two parts of the sentences.

1 My son's just failed another exam. I hope he doesn't *drop out*
2 I want to *stay on*
3 My daughter *comes back*
4 Do you *get off*
5 I didn't finish the last question in the exam – I *ran out*
6 No interesting job offers have *turned up*,
7 I'm only 23, so I don't plan to *settle down*
8 Everyone in this shop *clocks on*

a at 8 a.m., even the manager!
b at school, but I need to earn some money.
c for many years.
d from college every weekend with her laundry!
e of time!
f of university.
g so I'm applying for a place at college.
h work earlier on Fridays?

2 Complete these sentences with some of the phrasal verbs from Exercise 1.

1 Could I borrow a pen? Mine has .... of ink.
2 I hate my new job! Can I .... and work for you again?
3 We had an interview arranged, but the candidate didn't ....
4 Don't .... just because things are getting difficult.
5 Can you .... work this afternoon? I need your help at home.
6 Young people seem to .... at a much older age nowadays.

Learning skills recording new words (1)

3 Look at the strategies (a–e). Write notes for these words. Which information helps you remember how to use the word? Which do you usually record in your notebook?

hard-working: ....

full-time: ....

enclose: ....

a how to say it in your own language
b how to pronounce it
c what kind of word it is (noun, adjective, verb, adverb)
d how to use it (example sentences)
e when to use it (in writing or speaking)

4 Organising new words into groups can help you remember them. How many words from Unit 4 can you add to each group?

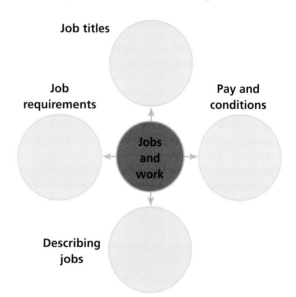

Check!

5 Answer these questions. Then use the first letters of five of the answers to give the name of a country from Unit 4.

1 If you don't like your current job, look for a .... one.
2 Something every child has when they think about their future: ....
3 Another word for a plan you have made: something you .... to do.
4 A place where workers mass-produce things: ....
5 A place you can go to learn how to be a mechanic, for example: ....
6 All employers want their employees to be this: ....

	1	2	3	4	5	6
Letters						
Word						

Unit 5 Travel

5a Business or pleasure?

Vocabulary travel tips

1 Complete the travel tips with these words.

> delays   local transport   luggage   plan
> round-the-world trip   travel   trip

TIPS FOR TRAVELLERS

➤ ¹ _____ light – don't take
unnecessary ² _____ .

➤ Relax – don't get stressed by
³ _____ .

➤ Use ⁴ _____ – it's cheaper and
more fun.

➤ ⁵ _____ well and get the most
from your ⁶ _____ .

➤ On a ⁷ _____ , it's often cheaper
to fly east to west.

2 Complete the sentences with the correct form of
journey, *travel* or *trip*.

1 I've just got back from an amazing
_____ to Greece.

2 We _____ right across Australia. It
took a week.

3 I love going on long train _____ .

4 We went on a few day _____ from
the resort.

5 How was your _____ ? Was there
much traffic on the motorway?

6 Air _____ is fast, but usually it's
quite expensive.

Reading a travel journalist

3 Read the interview with travel journalist Boyd
Matson. Write the number of the paragraph (1–5)
next to the question.

a Do you think we can avoid doing long-term
damage to some of the great travel
destinations?

b What is your most memorable travel experience?

c What have you learned from travelling with
your children?

d How much time do you spend on the road in a
typical year?

e What is your travel philosophy?

4 Read the interview again. Choose the correct
option or options (a–c).

1 Boyd Matson travels
a in his work.
b for pleasure.
c for family reasons.

2 He became interested in travelling
a a long time ago.
b recently.
c when he worked for NBC News.

3 He thinks that travel is
a dangerous.
b fun.
c risky.

4 When travelling, he prefers to
a experience new things.
b observe people.
c take part in things.

5 Find expressions in the text which mean:

1 like something very much
_____

2 be optimistic when things go wrong
_____

3 love doing something
_____

4 see the same things differently
_____

Grammar present perfect simple and past simple

6 Look at the time expressions and complete the
sentences about Boyd Matson with the present
perfect simple and past simple form of the verbs.

1 Boyd Matson _____ (work) for
National Geographic for years.

2 He _____ (write) hundreds of
articles in his career.

3 He _____ (take) his kids to
Machu Picchu a few years ago.

4 He _____ (not / have) any
life-threatening experiences so far.

5 He _____ (have) an interesting
time in Morocco last summer.

6 He _____ (be) on a working trip
to Egypt this month.

One on One

Adventure journalist Boyd Matson believes in taking chances.

Business or pleasure?
By Keith Bellows

Boyd Matson is one of the great travel journalists of our day. I've been a big fan of his work for years and I've 'travelled' to many places through his reports, radio shows and news columns. No stranger to adventure, Matson has suffered dehydration, broken bones, snakebite and countless other troubles on his trips – and usually comes up laughing. For the past two years, his highly popular column *Unbound* has appeared in *National Geographic Traveler* magazine.

What is it about travel that you love?

I've been addicted to travel since I was a kid. I read a book about Chinese political leaders and a book about a missionary's experience in New Guinea. I thought, I want to go to China and New Guinea to see what they're like for myself.

1 Probably a third of the time. When I worked for NBC News years ago, I travelled half the time or more. I was single then! Now I'm married with a family.

2 My kids have helped me to open my eyes and see things from a fresh angle. When my kids were younger, I gave one of them a camera and one a video camera. It was fun to compare their shots to my own and see how they saw things in a slightly different way.

3 I'm optimistic that people increasingly are aware that we have to do something, and I've seen small changes. Unfortunately, I've also seen places with serious damage. I've been to iconic, internationally famous spots where, just out of sight, they are dumping all the rubbish the tourists have left behind.

4 One of the greatest experiences of my life was the trip to Khumbu Icefall on Mount Everest. Unfortunately, while we were there, the best-known Sherpa climber in the world was killed. It shows that while travel is a lot of fun, there are risks involved sometimes. You have to be careful but enjoy it while you're there.

5 I want to go to new places in a way that gives me a better experience, not to go as an observer but as a participant. So I guess that is my philosophy of travel: Get off the tour bus.

Glossary
dehydration (n) /ˌdihaɪˈdreɪʃn/ when you do not have enough water in your body

---

7 Complete the conversation with the present perfect simple and past simple form of the verbs.

A: ¹ _____ you _____ (do) a lot of travelling?

B: Well, that depends what you mean by 'a lot'! I ² _____ (go) to about six or seven countries, I suppose.

A: That's a lot! I ³ _____ (not / be) to that many. Where ⁴ _____ you _____ (go) on your last trip?

B: The last place I ⁵ _____ (go) to was Iceland. That was a couple of months ago.

A: Oh, I ⁶ _____ (always / want) to go there. I'd love to see those hot springs that bubble out of the ground.

B: The geysers? Yeah, we ⁷ _____ (see) one that shot up about twenty metres! It was spectacular.

A: Wow! So what's the most spectacular thing you ⁸ _____ (see), do you think?

B: Maybe Las Vegas. We ⁹ _____ (fly) over it at night when we ¹⁰ _____ (be) on our way to Los Angeles. It was glowing! It ¹¹ _____ (look) like a film set.

8 Pronunciation *has, have*

🔊 **1.26** Listen to these sentences. Notice the pronunciation of *has* /həz/ and *have* /həv/. Then repeat the sentences.

1 Matson has suffered many troubles on his trips.

2 His column *Unbound* has appeared in *Traveler* magazine.

3 They dump the rubbish the tourists have left behind.

4 My kids have helped me to open my eyes.

5b Where to go, what to do there

Vocabulary holiday destinations

1 Complete the sentences from a travel agent's brochure with these words.

busy	crowded	exotic	peaceful	relaxing
remote	safe	tropical	unspoilt	vibrant

1 Explore the _____ streets and _____ markets of this _____ city.

2 Get away from it all on a luxury break in _____ surroundings.

3 Leave stress behind and recharge your batteries in the _____ setting of a _____ village high in the mountains.

4 Family-friendly holidays in _____ resorts on the Mediterranean.

5 The holiday of a lifetime: _____ beaches, _____ scenery. Unforgettable.

6 Take a trip along the _____ coastline of southern Australia.

Listening top film locations

2 🔊 **1.27** Listen to a travel show about holidays in film locations. Which of these places do they mention? What kind of films are made in these places?

Hollywood	action
London	comedy
Monument Valley	drama
New Zealand	romance
Paris	science fiction
Prague	western

3 🔊 **1.27** Listen again. Tick (✓) the activities the speakers mention. Where can you do these things?

1 stay in a famous hotel
2 go on a tour with a local guide
3 go up in a hot-air balloon
4 visit a film studio
5 go sightseeing in the Old Town
6 take a walking tour

4 🔊 **1.27** Listen again. Answer the questions.

1 How long have people been making westerns in Monument Valley?

2 How long have the Navajo people lived in Monument Valley?

3 According to the presenter, what's the best way to see Monument Valley?

4 When did film stars start going to Prague?

5 Why is it easier to get to Prague now?

6 Which film features King's Cross Station?

Glossary
sandstone (n) /ˈsænstəʊn/ rock which is made of sand
Navajo Nation (n) /ˈnɑvəhəʊ ˈneɪʃn/ Native America territory

Grammar present perfect continuous and simple, *How long … ?*

5 Complete the comments from visitors to the film locations. Use the present perfect simple and the present perfect continuous forms of the verbs.

1 We _____ (walk) around London all day – we _____ (see) every Harry Potter site!

2 The guide _____ (tell) us about the film stars he _____ (meet).

3 I _____ (take) photos of this amazing scenery, but my battery _____ (just / run out).

4 We _____ (wait) for the weather to change so the balloon can take off – we _____ (pay) for our tickets now, so I hope we can go up.

5 I _____ (explore) Prague on my own. I _____ (find) some lovely quiet corners.

6 Let's get a coffee. We _____ (not / have) anything to drink and we _____ (sightsee) since first thing this morning.

6 Rewrite the sentences using the words in brackets. Use the present perfect simple or the present perfect continuous, as appropriate.

1 I came to the beach after breakfast. Now it's suppertime.

_____

(lie / all day)

2 We set off at seven. It's now three o'clock.

_____

(travel)

3 We first came here ten years ago. We come every year.

_____

(come)

4 I started this book when I arrived. I haven't finished it yet.

_____

(read)

5 I left Paris this morning. Now I'm in Rome.

_____

(drive / 1,000 kilometres)

6 This is our third hotel this holiday!

_____

(stay)

7 Write questions with *How long* and the present perfect continuous for sentences 1–4 in Exercise 6. Then write the answers.

1 _____

2 _____

3 _____

4 _____

8 Dictation *How long … ?*

1.28 Listen and write the questions. Then complete the answers for yourself.

1 Q: _____
A: _____

2 Q: _____
A: _____

3 Q: _____
A: _____

4 Q: _____
A: _____

5 Q: _____
A: _____

6 Q: _____
A: _____

5c The responsible traveller

Listening a radio phone-in

1 🔊 **1.29** You are going to listen to a radio phone-in about travelling and conservation issues. Tick (✓) the words you think you will hear. Then listen and check.

> fuel   environment   extinct   in-flight magazine
> driving   budget airlines   statistics
> common sense   worry   improve   tax
> communities

2 🔊 **1.29** Listen again. Complete the questions the listeners ask.

1   Is flying greener than .... ?
2   Is it possible to go on an eco-friendly .... ?
3   Can I be an '........................' in Madagascar?

3 What answers did the expert give? Choose the correct option (a–b).

1   a   It's better to fly for short distances.
    b   Statistics can be confusing. Use your common sense.

2   a   The Internet can give you information about these cruises.
    b   All big operators run this type of cruise.

3   a   Madagascar has a growing eco-tourism industry.
    b   Only tourists working on conservation projects can visit Madagascar.

Vocabulary conservation

4 Look at these words. Find and write:

> eco-friendly   habitats   impact   issues
> projects   species   waste

1   two words which can follow:
    a   conservation .... ,
        conservation ....
    b   threatened .... ,
        threatened ....

2   words which mean the same as:
    a   rubbish: ....
    b   green: ....
    c   effect: ....

Word focus *thing*

5 Match the extracts from the radio programme (1–4) with the uses of the expressions with *thing* (a–d).

1   Andrew Marshall, an expert in […] all things green.
2   But I think the best thing is to use your common sense.
3   Tour operators have been taking steps to improve things in this area.
4   The thing is, there are lot of problems […] there.

a   giving advice
b   introducing a problem or explanation
c   talking about general aspects of something
d   referring to a group of unspecified ideas, objects, etc.

6 Complete the sentences with these expressions with *thing*.

> a few things   and things   best thing
> important thing   sort of thing   worst thing

1   I love visiting old churches ....
2   We're almost ready to go. I just need to sort .... out.
3   The .... about this rubbish is that it takes years to disappear.
4   She's really into conservation and that ....
5   The .... about France is the food.
6   The .... is to check with the tour operator.

5d Is something wrong?

Vocabulary travel problems

1 Make compound nouns with these words.

| allowance | card | control | documents |
| hire | poisoning | room | timetable |

1 baggage ....
2 boarding ....
3 car ....
4 food ....
5 hotel ....
6 passport ....
7 travel ....
8 train ....

2 Complete the sentences with the compound nouns from Exercise 1.

1 I've left the .... at home, so I hope the times are on our tickets.

2 You can't go back now – you've been through ....

3 Our .... is right above the hotel kitchen!

4 Did they write the gate number on the .... when we checked in?

5 We've had to pay extra because we went over our ....

6 I've got some medicine with me in case I get ....

7 Excuse me, where are the .... offices? Are they outside?

8 Keep all your .... in a safe place.

Real life dealing with problems

3 Match the comments (1–6) with the responses (a–f). Write T next to the things a tourist would say.

1 Can I help?
2 Why have we been waiting so long?
3 I wonder if you could help us?
4 Is there anything you can do about the air-conditioning?
5 I'm sorry, but I've lost the key to my room.
6 Is anything wrong?

a Don't worry. I'll give you another one.
b I hope so. It's about the noise from the room next door.
c I'll ask someone to take a look at it. Which room is it?
d Yes, I've left my bag with all my travel documents somewhere.
e Yes, of course. What's the problem?
f I'm afraid the flight has been delayed.

4 Pronunciation strong and weak forms

🔊 **1.30** Complete the exchanges with these prepositions. Then listen and repeat.

| at | for | from |

1 A: Which gate are you .... ?
   B: I'm .... gate 17.

2 A: Where have these people come .... ?
   B: They're .... the other bus – it broke down.

3 A: How long are you here .... ?
   B: .... another week.

5 Listen and respond travel situations

🔊 **1.31** Listen to comments in travel situations. Respond with your own words using the word in brackets. Then compare your response with the model answer that follows.

1

> *Is anything wrong?*

> *Yes, I've lost my passport.*

1 (passport)
2 (problem)
3 (ages)
4 (manager)
5 (hope)

5e Hello from Egypt!

Writing a postcard

1 Writing skill informal style

a What do these informal expressions mean? Write them in the correct place.

> awesome   cool   no way   wow

1   I don't believe it / you. ....
2   I'm surprised. ....
3   I agree / approve. ....
4   That's incredible / amazing / impressive. ....

b What do these abbreviations mean? Write them in the correct place.

> BF   GF   LOL   oxox   thx

1   thank you: ....
2   hugs and kisses (to end a message): ....
3   laugh out loud (to say you found something funny): ....
4   boyfriend: ....
5   girlfriend: ....

c Add exclamation marks to these sentences where appropriate.

1   The resort is fine.
2   The beach is gorgeous.
3   The journey was exhausting.
4   I'm quite tired.
5   I love it here.

d Rewrite these sentences from a postcard as full sentences.

1   Food here delicious.

2   Been on a camel ride (bumpy!).

3   Never been so hot in my life!

4   Taking it easy today cos did too much yesterday.

5   Photos in the usual place online.

e Rewrite these sentences in a more informal style.

1   The weather here is fantastic.

2   We've been lying by the hotel pool since we arrived.

3   I'm thinking of staying an extra week because it's so beautiful.

4   We've arranged to go on a couple of day trips.

5   We had a terrible flight. There was a long delay, the seats were uncomfortable and there was no food!

2 Write a postcard from Egypt. Use the questions as a guide.

- What was the journey like?
- What's the weather like?
- What's the hotel like?
- What are the people like?
- What's the food like?

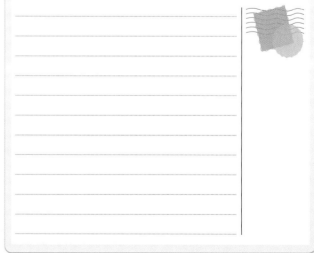

Wordbuilding compound nouns (noun + noun)

> ▶ **WORDBUILDING compound nouns (noun + noun)**
>
> We can use two nouns together to mean one thing.
> *baggage allowances*
> *boarding cards*
> Compound nouns can be made up of two words (*boarding card*), one word (*backpack*) or two words with a hyphen (*sky-diving*). The plural is made by making the second noun plural (*hotel rooms*, not *hotels room*).

1 Write the compound nouns in three groups.

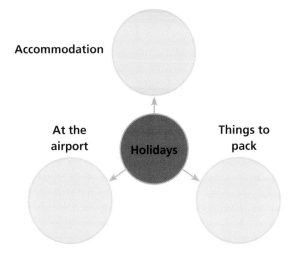

arrivals hall	hand luggage
baggage reclaim	insect repellent
budget hotel	money belt
campsite	sun cream
departure lounge	travel tablets
guest house	youth hostel

2 Write the names of these things.

1 A couple of these can stop you feeling ill:

2 Essential if you want to avoid itchy bites:

3 Good value accommodation and not just for young people:

4 Not very luxurious, and you need your own tent:

5 Where you pick up your cases after leaving the plane:

6 You can take this on the plane:

7 A good idea if you are in dangerous areas:

8 Don't forget to put this on exposed areas of skin:

Learning skills dictionary skills

> A good dictionary gives you information about how a word is used as well as its meaning. This helps you to choose between confusing words.

3 Complete the dictionary definitions with the word they define: *travel* or *trip*.

1 _____ (n) (countable) the act of going somewhere and coming back again, usually for a short time *We've been on a day _____ to the capital.*
2 _____ (v) to go from one place to another, usually in a vehicle *We _____ by train a lot when we were in India.* (n) (uncountable) the activity of visiting different places *They say _____ is good for you.*

4 Find these words in your dictionary: *journey, tour* and *trip*. Then complete these sentences.

1 I've been on a sightseeing _____ around the island.

2 The _____ across the Indian Ocean took a couple of weeks.

3 What was the _____ to Paris like? Did you stop on the way?

4 I've been reading about James Cook's first _____ to the East.

Check!

5 Solve the anagrams to find words from Student's Book Unit 5.

1 a d e l s y
   you often get them at airports: _____

2 a a d e h i k l m o r s y
   people who are on a trip for pleasure, not work:
   _____

3 a a b h i s t t
   wildlife homes: _____

4 i m o o q s t u
   be careful it doesn't bite you: _____

5 f g i n r s u
   do it at the beach: _____

6 c e i k t t
   you can't travel without buying one: _____

7 c e i m o o r s t u -
   low-impact travel: _____

8 a d e i i n n o s t t
   the place you go to: _____

Unit 6 Wellbeing

6a Natural foods

Vocabulary food

1 Complete the table with the names of these foods.

Natural food	Food made from other ingredients

Word focus *make*

2 🔊 **1.32** Listen to two people discussing a cooking dilemma. Complete the sentences.

1 Are you going to ___*make*___ something?
2 Because it will help you to make _____ .
3 I still want to make _____ .
4 I could make cheese soufflé or prawn curry or just a _____ .
5 Can I make a _____ ?
6 All this talk about food is making _____ !

3 Add the expressions from Exercise 2 to the patterns (a–e).

a **make** (to produce something): *lunch, something,* _____

b **make** + noun (an action, to do something): *a plan, a mess,* _____

c **make** + *somebody* + noun (to do something for someone): *me a sandwich, you a drink,* _____

d **make** + *somebody* + adjective (to cause something): *me ill, you better,* _____

e other expressions: *make something up, make sense,* _____

4 Complete the sentences with expressions from Exercises 2 and 3.

1 I'm feeling a bit stressed. I have to _____ for ten people today!
2 Look at the state of the kitchen! Why must you always _____ when you cook?
3 I can't eat much chocolate. It _____ – it gives me a headache.
4 Are you thirsty? Can I _____ ?
5 I don't understand this recipe at all. It just doesn't _____ .
6 I'm hungry, but I can't _____ what to eat.

Listening bush tucker

7 Which sentence (a–c) best reflects the speaker's opinion?

   a Bush tucker only gives you part of the food you need.

   b The things you can eat in the outback are nutritious but taste horrible.

   c You don't have to look very hard to find food in the outback.

Grammar modal verbs (1)

8 Rewrite the visitor information from a national park with modal verbs. Sometimes more than one answer is possible.

> **1** Camping in the park is not allowed.
>
> **2** Picnics are restricted to designated areas.
>
> **3** Do not swim in the rivers.
>
> **4** It's a good idea to carry water with you.
>
> **5** Inform the warden in advance of your visit.
>
> **6** It's not necessary to show identification on entry.
>
> **7** Approaching wild animals is not advisable.
>
> **8** Report any accidents or incidents with wild animals.

1 _____

2 _____

3 _____

4 _____

5 _____

6 _____

7 _____

8 _____

5 🎵 **1.33** You are going to hear about an unusual eating experience. First, underline the option you think is correct. Then listen and check.

  1 Darwin is in the *north / south* of Australia.

  2 The native people of Australia are known as *Aboriginal people / Maori*.

  3 Crocodile meat is *edible / poisonous*.

  4 The native people of Australia are known for *collecting / growing* their food.

6 🎵 **1.33** Listen again. Tick (✓) the things the speaker ate.

ants	crocodile eggs	crocodile meat	grass
leaves	lemons	trees	water lilies

Glossary

the outback (n) /ðiˈaʊtbæk/ the desert areas of Australia where few people live

watering hole (n) /ˈwɔːtrɪŋ həʊl/ a small pool of water where animals go to drink

9 Pronunciation weak forms

🎵 **1.34** Listen and repeat the sentences. Pay attention to how *to* is not stressed.

6b Strategies for success

Reading willpower

1 Read the article and answer the quiz questions.

2 Read the article again and find words that mean:

1 an objective, an aim (n): _____

2 people (n): _____

3 decisions or promises you make to yourself (n): _____

4 without fear, courageous (adj): _____

5 tests of your abilities (n): _____

6 a starting point or basis for something (n): _____

3 Match these missing sentences with the three quotes at the end of the article.

1 If you don't take a risk, you won't know what you're capable of.

2 You can develop your willpower if you want to.

3 If you give up, everyone will give up.

Grammar first conditional; *when, as soon as, unless, until, before*

4 Write full sentences with the present simple and *will* + infinitive.

1 you make a healthy meal / feel better afterwards

2 I watch a movie / enjoy myself

3 you find a new route to work / save money

4 you take chewing gum with you / not smoke

5 not buy chocolate / not eat it

6 live longer / have a good diet

5 Rewrite the sentences with the word in brackets without changing the meaning.

1 You won't achieve anything if you don't take risks. (unless)

2 Your friends will help you if you ask them. (as soon as)

3 You'll be successful if you plan things carefully. (when)

4 You won't know what you can do if you don't try. (until)

5 You'll make a lot of mistakes and then you'll succeed. (before)

6 You won't save any money unless you have a plan. (if)

Vocabulary a healthy lifestyle

6 Which of these strategies are not part of a healthy lifestyle?

changing bad habits
cutting down on relaxation
avoiding outdoor activities
giving up junk food
taking up smoking
cutting out fatty food

7 Dictation healthy living

🔊 **1.35** Listen and write the sentence halves (1–4, a–d). Then match the halves to make logical sentences.

1 _____

2 _____

3 _____

4 _____

a _____

b _____

c _____

d _____

Strategies for success

Every month you pay a large sum of money for your membership of the local gym. But some months you don't even go. Sound familiar? What does it take to achieve a goal? Why do some determined individuals pull their boots on and achieve what few would even dare to try? Find out the secrets of three successful adventurers below. But first, imagine you want to make some changes in your life: do our quiz and check out how much willpower you have.

1 You get home after a long day at work. What do you do for your evening meal?
 a make a healthy meal using fresh ingredients
 b phone out for a delivery of fast food
 c defrost a processed 'ready meal'

2 Summer is coming and you want to look your best. You've got a free evening ahead. Do you … ?
 a go out jogging
 b read a magazine about healthy living
 c watch a movie

3 You've been spending too much money recently. Your route to work takes you through a shopping mall. Do you … ?
 a find a different route that avoids shops
 b take the usual route and buy yourself something nice
 c take the usual route but not spend any money

4 You decided to give up smoking a while ago. You're going out with friends. Do you … ?
 a take some chewing gum with you
 b leave your cigarettes at home (you'll be able to smoke your friends')
 c take three cigarettes with you

If your answers are mostly **a**, you'll probably stick to your resolutions. If your answers are mostly **c**, you have the will but perhaps not enough power. If your answers are mostly **b**, you'd better read what the experts say. You don't have to be an intrepid adventurer to find these comments useful. We're all faced with challenges, big and small, in our everyday lives.

Mental challenges are as difficult to pass as endurance tests. You pass through failure to success. You do not avoid failure. To me, the most exciting time is when things aren't going right. As a leader, you can't give up.

Robert D. Ballard, marine explorer

When I had to decide between the comfort of a staff news job and the risk of freelance photography, my mother told me that no great chasm was ever leaped in two small jumps.

Jodi Cobb, National Geographic *photographer*

People can build their willpower deliberately. We are born with a certain amount, but that is just a platform. I think you can build willpower and be strong and achieve a lot. Start with a step you feel comfortable with and take it one step ahead.

Børge Ousland, polar explorer

Glossary
chasm (n) /'kæzm / a long deep narrow hole in ice or rock
dare (v) /dɛː/ be brave enough to do something
endurance (n) /ɪn'djʊərns/ the ability to keep doing something difficult, unpleasant or painful for a long time

6c Alternative lifestyles

Vocabulary modern life

1 Circle the correct option to make things associated with a 24-hour society.

1 *electric / natural* light
2 *high / low* blood pressure
3 *outdoor / indoor* jobs
4 *day / night* work schedules
5 *irregular / regular* sleep

Listening alternative lifestyles

2 💿 **1.36** Listen to a radio programme and choose the correct option (a–c).

1 Lisa Napoli went to … .
   a Nepal
   b Tibet
   c Bhutan

2 She went there to … .
   a work
   b visit friends
   c go backpacking

3 As a result of her experience, she … .
   a became rich
   b learned to be content
   c gave up her job

4 Mark Boyle … .
   a changed his job
   b stayed in his local environment
   c tried to live in a new culture

5 He decided to give up … .
   a eating meat
   b all his possessions
   c using money

6 He learned the importance of … .
   a work
   b people
   c possessions

3 Which statement(s) (a–c) agree(s) with what the presenter said?

a Both Napoli and Boyle found they were happier with fewer material things.
b Neither Napoli nor Boyle was able to give up the 24-hour lifestyle.
c Napoli and Boyle's experiences are not applicable to anyone else.

4 Grammar extra questions with *how*

> ▶ **QUESTIONS WITH *HOW***
>
> We can use *how* before a verb, before an adjective or before an adverb in questions.

a Look at the questions from the radio programme. What kind of word follows *How*?

1 How easy is it? _____
2 How quickly can we adapt to a different culture? _____
3 How determined do you have to be? _____
4 How realistic is it to make changes like this? _____
5 How did he manage? _____

b Write these words with the questions (1–6). Then match the questions with the answers (a–f).

| badly | difficult | far | long | quickly | soon |

1 How _____ was it to give up money?
2 How _____ is Bhutan from the United States?
3 How _____ does it take to fly to Bhutan?
4 How _____ did they do in the exam?
5 How _____ is the oil running out?
6 How _____ can you get here?

a About ten hours.
b Almost three thousand kilometres.
c Disastrously!
d Give me an hour.
e It was quite easy, actually.
f That depends on which experts you believe.

6d Eating out

Vocabulary restaurants

1 Put the restaurant customer's words in order to make statements and questions.

1 from / that / made / what's

.... ?

2 taste / they / like / what / do

.... ?

3 I'll / think / that / try / I

....

4 come / does / with / vegetables / it

.... ?

5 the / have / same / I'll

....

2 Grammar extra *need to*

> ▶ **NEED TO**
>
> We can use *need to* to say that it's important or necessary, rather than obligatory, to do something.
> *Is that restaurant busy at lunchtime? Do we need to book a table?*
>
> We can use *need to* when *have to* or *must* would sound too strong.
>
> *Don't need to* means it's not necessary to do something or that you can choose not to do it.
> *You don't need to have a starter if you don't want one.*

Complete the sentences with *need to* or *have to*.

1 Do we .... wait for the waiter to show us our table? (necessary)

2 You .... dress up – it's a pretty casual place. (not necessary)

3 It's a bit posh – you .... wear a jacket and tie. (obligatory)

4 They don't accept advance bookings. You .... stand in a queue if it's busy. (obligatory)

5 You .... leave a tip – the service charge is included in the bill. (not necessary)

Real life describing dishes

3 Which is the odd word out in the sentences describing dishes?

1 It's a bit like *potatoes / lamb / baked*.
2 They taste *salty / fish / spicy*.
3 It's made from *meat / vegetables / hot*.
4 It's a kind of *bland / boiled / fried* dish.

4 Read the comments. Is the person describing a starter (S), main course (M) or dessert (D)?

1 It's made of milk and it's quite sweet. It's usually served cold.
2 They're sort of little packets of vegetables. They're quite spicy.
3 It's a baked dish made from different kinds of meat and vegetables, with rice or pasta.
4 It tastes quite salty. It's a sort of spread for bread or toast.

5 Pronunciation disappearing sounds

a 🔊 1.37 Listen to the sentences with these words. Cross out the part of the word which is not pronounced – the disappearing sound – in each word. Then listen again and repeat the sentences.

1 comfortable   3 national
2 evening   4 travelling

b 🔊 1.38 How do you pronounce these words from Student's Book Units 3–6? Listen and repeat.

> beverage   camera   poisoning   several
> snorkelling

6 Listen and respond talking to a waiter

🔊 1.39 Listen to the waiter's questions. Respond with your own words. Then compare your response with the model answer that follows.

1
> Are you ready to order?

> Not quite. We just need a minute.

6e A fitness centre

Writing a formal letter

1 Writing skill explaining consequences

a Your local fitness centre was refurbished recently and as part of this process there have been other changes. Look at the notes and write these headings in the correct spaces (1–3).

cafeteria	opening times	prices

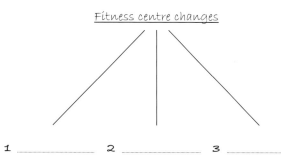

Fitness centre changes

1 _____   2 _____   3 _____

a 9 a.m. – not early enough

b too expensive for families

c no discounts for retired people

d complicated multi-ticket scheme

e should be open to public

b Match the sentence halves. Then complete the sentences using these expressions for explaining consequences.

Consequently	has led to	means that
therefore	will result in	

1 The swimming pool doesn't open until 9 a.m.,

2 Taking away the discounts for retired people

3 The multi-ticket scheme is too complicated.

4 Opening the cafeteria to the public

5 The price increase

a fewer families using the centre now.

b people don't take advantage of offers.

c people can't go swimming before they go to work.

d they can't afford to use the centre very often.

e more people using the centre.

2 Use the information from Exercise 1b to complete this letter. Refer to Student's Book and Workbook Unit 4 to review formal style.

Dear Sir,

We are writing to express our concern at the recent changes to Newton Fitness Centre. We are concerned about _____

_____

In our view, _____

_____

_____

We also note that _____

_____

In addition, _____

_____

Finally, we feel that _____

_____

We request that you review these changes to the services that the fitness centre provides to local residents.

Yours sincerely

PH Singh

PH Singh
Newton Residents' Association

Wordbuilding phrasal verbs

> ▶ **WORDBUILDING phrasal verbs**
>
> Phrasal verbs with *down* and *up* often describe change.
> *cut down   give up*

1 Complete the sentences with the correct form of these verbs and *up*.

> go   grow   put   speed
> take

1 The prices in the café have .... since we were last here.

2 They've .... some abstract paintings. It looks really different now.

3 I think I'll .... cookery this winter.

4 If this bus doesn't .... a bit, we'll be late.

5 You should .... a bit and stop behaving like a child.

2 Complete the sentences with the correct form of these verbs and *down*.

> bring   come   get   slow
> take

1 Strawberries are expensive now, but the price will .... in the summer.

2 I'm on a diet because I have to .... my weight ....

3 You'll have an accident unless you ....

4 We can't .... these warning notices .... – they have to be visible at all times.

5 There's a danger that the protests will .... the government.

Learning skills planning writing

3 Look at the list of strategies for planning writing. Which strategies has this student used?

- noting down the questions your writing needs to answer
- noting down the purpose of your written text
- thinking about who the reader is
- brainstorming ideas
- brainstorming useful vocabulary or other language
- using a mind map to organise words
- organising words in a table
- following a model text
- listing standard useful expressions
- listing useful linking words
- writing notes and short sentences
- organising sentences by sequence or idea
- writing the same idea in different ways

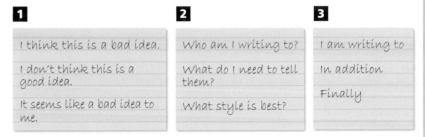

1
I think this is a bad idea.
I don't think this is a good idea.
It seems like a bad idea to me.

2
Who am I writing to?
What do I need to tell them?
What style is best?

3
I am writing to
In addition
Finally

4 Which of the strategies in Exercise 3 have you used when you have had to write something in English?

5 Answer the questions with reference to the writing you have done for the writing tasks in Student's Book and Workbook Units 1–6?

1 Which of the strategies did you use?
2 How helpful did you find them?
3 Is your writing more successful if you plan it first?
4 Which is the most useful strategy for you? Why?

Check!

6 Complete the crossword with the answers to the clues. All these words are in Student's Book Unit 6.

1 A strong-smelling Asian fruit.
2 Crisps, sweets, salty snacks, etc.
3 Something in food and drink that increases blood pressure.
4 If food is not yet cooked, it's …. .
5 Another name for a savoury banana.
6, 7, 8 A cheese that has EU Guaranteed Traditional Speciality status.

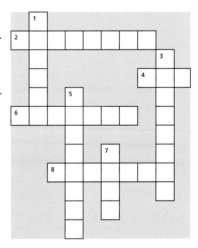

Unit 7 Living space

7a Longhouses

Vocabulary and reading
features of homes

1 Look at the photos. Tick (✓) which of these things
you think you would find in the houses. Then read
the article and check your answers.

> attic   balcony   basement   central heating
> double glazing   fireplace   garage   garden
> terrace   veranda

2 Read the article again. Answer the questions.

1   Where can you find longhouses?

2   Which parts of a longhouse were for animals?

3   Where did the inhabitants of longhouses cook?

4   Which type of longhouse is still built today?

Grammar comparatives and
superlatives

3 Complete the article about longhouses with the
comparative and superlative forms.

4 Complete the sentences with comparative forms.

To show a process of change

1   Small apartments are becoming
    .... (popular).

2   Houses prices are getting
    .... (high).

3   They are building blocks of flats
    .... (fast).

**To show how two things change in relation to
each other**

4   .... (big) the windows,
    .... (bright) the rooms are.

5   .... (close) it is to the shops,
    .... (good).

6   .... (nice) the terrace is,
    .... (often) we'll use it.

5 Grammar extra modifying comparatives
and superlatives

> ▶ **MODIFYING COMPARATIVES and SUPERLATIVES**
>
> We use the following expressions to show the degree
> of difference between things we compare: *a bit, a little,
> a little bit, slightly, much, a lot, far, considerably.*
>
> We can use *easily* and *by far* to modify a superlative
> structure.

Put the words in the correct order and rewrite the
sentences.

1   one of / The longhouse / widespread / was /
    most / the / designs / home.

2   use / than / a lot / Ceiling fans / less /
    air-conditioning / electricity.

3   slightly / we / The rent / expected / is / than /
    higher.

4   is / today / the / by far / house / we've / best /
    This / seen.

5   makes / inviting / a house / a bit / look /
    A veranda /more.

6   lit / is / cosier / when / far / The room / is /
    the fire.

6 Pronunciation *as ... as*

🔊 1.40 Listen and repeat the sentences about a
new home.

1   The rent is as much as I can pay.
2   It's as spacious as my old house.
3   It isn't as dark as I thought.
4   The carpet looks as good as new.
5   The kitchen is as big as I need.

Longhouses

A reconstructed longhouse in Norway

The longhouse is a type of home that is found all over the world, from northern Europe across Asia and also in the Americas. As its name suggests, it's a building which is [1] _____ (long) than it is wide. The fact that this kind of structure is so widespread suggests that it was the [2] _____ (appropriate) in most environments and was also the [3] _____ (good) use of local materials. Although the basic idea is the same, there are several variations according to the different conditions around the world.

Traditional longhouses in Asia were homes to more than one family, although not all were as [4] _____ (crowded) as in one region of Nepal, where several generations of a large family could mean up to 50 people living together.

The main entrance to Indonesian longhouses is via steps up to a veranda, as the typical longhouse is built on stilts. In the hot climate, a house can cool down [5] _____ (easily) if it's built off the ground. This also means that any livestock can stay in the space under the longhouse, so they are [6] _____ (well) protected. In contrast, a Viking longhouse in northern Europe needed to be [7] _____ (hot) inside than outside. The [8] _____ (close) people were to the animals, the [9] _____ (warm) they were, so Viking longhouses had a section at one end for livestock.

Viking longhouses had one central fire for heat and for cooking, whereas in longhouses in [10] _____ (hot) climates the kitchens are typically built as an annexe apart from the main living area. This means the main rooms are [11] _____ (exposed) to the risk of fire. Indonesian longhouses have a central wall dividing the building into an open public area down one side and [12] _____ (private) rooms along the other side. Both European and Asian longhouses had attics for storage of things like food.

A longhouse in Borneo, Indonesia

Over the centuries, longhouse design has become more and [13] _____ (sophisticated), but they still remain the design for rural living in tropical areas. In Europe, on the other hand, longhouses were replaced by other architectural styles.

Glossary
livestock (n) /ˈlaɪvstɒk/ farm and domestic
  animals

7b In the past

Vocabulary in the city

1 Match these words with the words (1–11) with the same meaning.

> atmosphere built-up modern neighbourhood
> open spaces polluted public transport
> residents run-down skyscraper traffic

1 new, contemporary: ....

2 area, district: ....

3 buses and trains: ....

4 character and feel: ....

5 with lots of buildings: ....

6 dirty: ....

7 high-rise building: ....

8 inhabitants: ....

9 movement of cars and other vehicles:
....

10 neglected: ....

11 parks: ....

Grammar *used to, would* and past simple

2 Tick (✓) the sentences where *used to* can replace the past simple.

1 This area didn't have so many skyscrapers before.

2 The pollution here was much worse than it is now.

3 The local residents campaigned for better public transport.

4 The atmosphere wasn't so relaxed in the past.

5 A new modern district replaced the neglected centre.

6 There weren't as many crowded neighbourhoods.

3 Rewrite the sentences you ticked in Exercise 2 with *used to* or *didn't use to*.

....

....

....

....

4 Tick (✓) the sentences where *would* can replace *used to*.

1 When I was young, we used to live next to my school.

2 My friends and I used to play in the street.

3 There used to be a lot of traffic along this road.

4 I didn't use to like my neighbours.

5 A huge tree used to grow in front of our house.

6 We didn't use to go out if it was raining.

5 Rewrite the sentences from Exercise 4 with *would* where possible. Rewrite the other sentences with the past simple.

1 ....

2 ....

3 ....

4 ....

5 ....

6 ....

6 Dictation childhood

🔊 **1.41** Listen and write the sentences. Then write your own answers for the three questions.

1 ....

2 Q: ....

   A: ....

3 ....

4 Q: ....

   A: ....

5 ....

6 Q: ....

   A: ....

Listening Timbuktu

7 🔊 **1.42** Listen to a podcast about Timbuktu. Are these facts true (T) or false (F)?

Timbuktu used to be:
1 an important Islamic city.
2 a World Heritage Site.
3 a major trading centre.
4 a destination for religious scholars.
5 invaded regularly by Moroccan forces.

8 🔊 **1.42** Listen again. Complete these sentences.

1 Timbuktu used to be a place of
....
2 Timbuktu has a great .... of ancient manuscripts.
3 Important Islamic teachings on medicine and .... are here.
4 The city's .... was important in its history.
5 Timbuktu is on the .... Niger.
6 .... trains used to pass through the city.
7 The river brought cargoes of .... and slaves to the city.
8 After the 16th century, the .... began to leave Timbuktu.

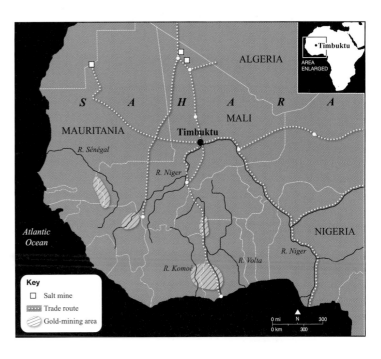

Glossary
cargoes (n) /ˈkɑːɡəʊz/ products being taken from one place to another on ships and aircraft
scholar (n) /ˈskɒlə/ an academic or specialist in a subject

7c Megacities

Listening 19.20.21

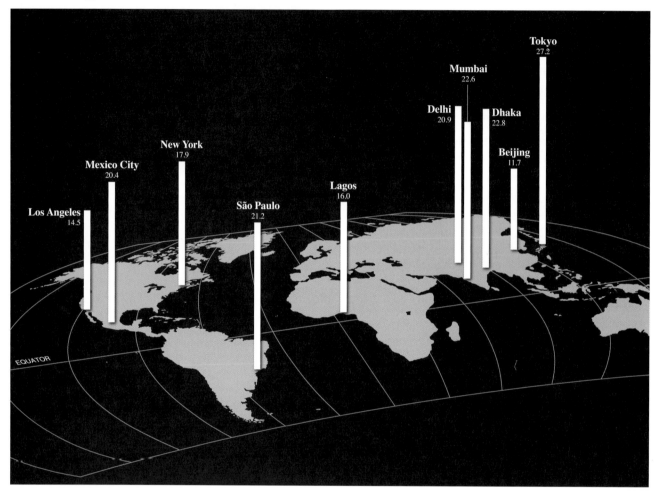

Population in millions

1 Can you name the five biggest cities in the world? Look at the map and check your ideas.

2 🎧 **1.43** You are going to listen to a podcast about a project called 19.20.21 by architect Richard Saul Wurman. What do you think the name 19.20.21 means? Listen and check your answer.

3 🎧 **1.43** Listen again. Tick (✓) the correct option or options (a–c).

　1　Why did Wurman begin the 19.20.21 project?
　　a　because cities are getting bigger and bigger
　　b　in order to understand more about the move to urban life
　　c　because he couldn't find enough information about cities

　2　Why do people keep moving to cities?
　　a　to get better opportunities
　　b　because that's where the important institutions are
　　c　because they have no choice

3 Why is a project like this needed?
　　a　so we can compare one city with another
　　b　so we understand cities and can improve them more successfully
　　c　because we don't know how to improve our cities

4 Complete the sentences with four of these places.

Beijing	Lagos	Los Angeles	Mumbai	Tokyo

　1　The biggest city in the world today is

　　_____ .

　2　_____ is the fastest growing city today.

　3　The most densely populated city is

　　_____ .

　4　_____ is the least dense city that covers the largest area.

7d Tea or coffee?

Real life expressing preferences

1 Grammar extra *prefer* and *would rather*

▶ PREFER and WOULD RATHER		
I prefer	+	verb + -ing noun to + infinitive
I'd prefer		noun to + infinitive
I'd rather		infinitive without to

We use the present simple form *prefer* to talk about things in general. We use the conditional form of *prefer* and *would rather* to talk about the future or a hypothetical situation.

Look at the grammar box. Then complete the sentences.

1   A: Do you usually get the bus to work?
    B: No. I prefer _____ (walk), especially when the weather is good.

2   A: Have you made your mind up about going out tonight?
    B: Yes. I'd prefer _____ (stay) in.

3   I _____ (prefer) action films to romances.

4   Do you prefer _____ (watch) TV or _____ (read) in the evenings?

5   A: Do you want a cup of tea?
    B: I'd rather _____ (have) coffee, actually.

6   A: Would you like tea?
    B: I _____ (prefer) coffee, if you have it.

2 Match the preferences (1–8) with the reasons (a–g). Then write full sentences.

Example:
1   *b I'd rather have tea in the evening because coffee keeps me awake.*

1   have tea / evening
2   swimming
3   have one long holiday
4   a job nearer home
5   rent than buy
6   reading the news online
7   small shops
8   driving a small car

a   big stores / less friendly
b   coffee / keep me awake
c   commuting / expensive
d   go / the gym / too tiring
e   not sure / stay here
f   it / more up-to-date
g   travel / further
h   use / less petrol

2   _____
3   _____
4   _____
5   _____
6   _____
7   _____
8   _____

3 Pronunciation rising and falling intonation

🔊 **1.44** Listen and repeat the questions. Notice how the intonation rises then falls.

1    2

3

4    5

4 Listen and respond preferences

🔊 **1.45** Listen to the questions. Respond with your own answer, giving a reason for your preference. Then compare your response with the model answer that follows.

1   *Do you usually get the bus or walk?*   *I prefer to walk because it's better for me.*

7e My city

Writing a description of a place

1 Read the introduction to a webpage. Then read the information about Amsterdam that a website reader has prepared. Match the website ideas (1–7) with the information (a–g).

a cycling around town (a daily activity) or into the nearby countryside. Rowing (on the Amstel River) is also a popular sport among the locals.

b how cosmopolitan it is. **As** almost 200 different nationalities live here, it's a very vibrant town with a broad range of cultural activities every day of the year … and all that within a village-like setting!

c it's one of the most multi-faceted cities in the world. Its cosmopolitan landscape, liberal mentality, world-class museums, stunning canals and fascinating history merge to exude a unique charm that's simply captivating.

d on the bridge that crosses the Groenburgwal canal. Amsterdam is very photogenic and there are many great spots for a memorable picture.

e the Begijnhof in the heart of Amsterdam – a tranquil place with beautiful houses and trees. It's simply the most magical place.

f the tallest men. The Dutch are some of the tallest people on this planet.

g the Van Gogh Museum (I'm a big fan of Van Gogh). But there are many others, **like** the Rijksmuseum with its stunning collection of Rembrandts.

Welcome to another edition of **I Love My City**. This week we have an insider's tour of **Amsterdam**.

Want to see your city on **Intelligent Travel**? Copy and paste our list of fill-in-the-blank ideas into an e-mail, fill in your answers, and send your responses (with any photos, videos or links) to IntelligentTravel@ngs.org.

1 The first place I take a visitor from out of town is …
2 If you come to my city, get your picture taken …
3 In my city, an active day outdoors involves …
4 My city's best museum is …
5 The most unexpected thing about my city is …
6 My city has …
7 My city should be featured on your website because …

2 Writing skill organising ideas

Match these categories (1–3) with the information (a–g) in Exercise 1.

1 places to see
2 things to do
3 general information

3 Word focus *as* and *like*

a Look at the highlighted words in the article. Choose the correct option.

1 as = *because / such as*
2 like = *because / such as*

b Complete the sentences about Amsterdam with *as* and *like*.

1 .... there are so many museums, there's lots to do on a rainy day.

2 Places .... Amsterdam are full of surprises.

3 .... it's so photogenic, it attracts lots of photographers.

4 People here love outdoor activities .... cycling and rowing.

5 It's great for cycling .... it's so flat.

6 At certain times of year .... spring, it's really beautiful.

4 Use the ideas in the article to write about your own town or city. Is your town or city similar to or different from Amsterdam?

Wordbuilding verb → adjective

> ▶ **WORDBUILDING verb → adjective**
>
> We can make adjectives from verbs by adding -ing.
> surround + -ing → surrounding streets
> run + n + -ing → running water
>
> We can use an adjective made from verb + -ing to define, explain or categorise the noun which follows it.
> surround +- -ing → surrounding streets = the streets that surround a place
> run + n +- -ing → running water = water that runs through pipes, i.e. tap water

1 Complete the sentences with adjectives made from these verbs.

> age entertain fill grow overhang
> refresh relax rise walk wind

1 The city centre is not the best place for a .... stroll!

2 The map shows all the best .... routes through the heart of the city.

3 We had an .... afternoon at the zoo.

4 There's a .... demand for cheaper apartments.

5 The park has a beautiful lake with .... trees.

6 This café is the best place for delicious and .... dishes.

7 People are moving out of the centre because of .... prices.

8 This district is home to an .... population now.

9 The atmosphere is a .... change from the main shopping area.

10 The gallery is at the end of a long and .... road.

2 Where in a house would you find these things?

1 a dining table: ....

2 a dressing gown: ....

3 a frying pan: ....

4 a rocking chair: ....

5 a sleeping bag: ....

6 a washing machine: ....

7 an ironing board: ....

8 shaving foam: ....

Learning skills understanding new words in context

> When you meet a new word, you can often guess its meaning. If you have a dictionary handy, you can look it up. However, many English words have several meanings. It helps if you can work out the relationship of the word to the other words in the sentence.

3 Look at the words in bold in these sentences which are connected with Student's Book page 87. Is each word an adjective (A), a noun (N) or a verb (V)?

1 The government transformed the **mining** zone into a national park.

2 As a child, I used to spend all my time **carrying** water.

3 Dofia Lala was **working** as a maid when she met the love of her life.

4 The shop filled with **working**-class men.

5 Ramos improvised songs about **growing** coffee.

6 I played the **recording** for my father.

4 Read these paragraphs. Are the words in bold adjectives (A), nouns (N) or verbs (V)?

> This is my village. The main [1] **building** in the village is the community centre. My house stands next to a [2] **rushing** river. We've got a big family [3] **gathering** here this weekend.
>
> It's Sunday evening in the city. There's a free concert in the park. Workmen are [4] **building** the stage and everyone's [5] **rushing** around. The technicians are checking the lights in the [6] **gathering** darkness.

5 What do the words in bold mean in your language? Check in a dictionary.

Check!

6 Answer these questions. The first letter of each answer spells a word. What it is is?

1 The city with a famous street called Fifth Avenue.

2 If you want to buy or sell a house, go to this person.

3 A shelter made of ice.

4 You might stay in one of these in Mongolia.

5 The natural environment of animal or plant.

6 Something modern houses are often made from. They are usually red or brown.

7 The opposite of *inside*.

8 The opposite of *rural* – an adjective describing cities.

9 This is an option if you don't want to buy a house.

10 They are extremely tall and there are lots of them in the answer to question 1.

1	
2	
3	
4	
5	
6	
7	
8	
9	
10	

Unit 8 Weird news

8a News

Reading nature news review

1 Read the article and complete the notes.

	What kind of animal is it?	Where was it found?	What's unusual about it?
1			
2			
3			

2 Read the article again. Then read this information about each animal. What is speculation (S) and what is certain (C)?

1 The handfish
   a walks on the seabed.
   b eats worms.
   c has toxic skin.

2 The 'Yoda' bat
   d is a newly found species.
   e eats fruit.
   f is a key part of the forest eco-system.

3 The squidworm
   g is a type of worm.
   h is the first in a new family of worms.

3 Find these words in the article.

1 two terms for the bottom of the sea
   .... , ...

2 a word that means 'samples or representative things'
   ....

3 a scientific term that means 'a group of individuals that can't be subdivided into smaller groups'
   ....

4 a word for animals that kill and eat other animals
   ....

5 a word that means 'poisonous'
   ....

6 an adjective that means 'from/in/of the sea'
   ....

7 a word that means 'sections'
   ....

Grammar speculation and deduction about the present

4 Read the clues and decide which of these things they describe. Write sentences using *might/could* and *must*. Use the plural form of one of the words.

| ants   bird   butterfly   lake   leaf   ocean |
| shark   spiders   stem   whale |

1 It has two legs, two wings and a tail. It can fly.
   ....

2 It's part of a plant. It's green.
   ....

3 It's a body of water. It's not salty. It's surrounded by land.
   ....

4 They are quite small and eat insects. They have eight legs. Some make webs.
   ....

5 It lives in water. It has fins and a tail. It's pretty big.
   ....

Word focus *look*

5 Complete the sentences with the correct form of *look*. Use *as though* or *like* where necessary.

1 These fins .... hands.
2 .... closely at these tentacles.
3 This bat .... it's from a film.
4 This fish .... odd.

6 Match the comments (1–5) and responses (a–e) with *look* to make logical exchanges.

1 Are you going on a whale-watching trip?
2 Have you seen my bag? I can't find it.
3 I think we should leave tomorrow.
4 It's been great, thanks. See you next year.
5 Look out! You're about to step on a spider!

a Look, let's talk about it later.
b No. What does it look like?
c OK, look after yourself!
d What? Where?
e Yes. We're really looking forward to it.

Isn't that weird?

1 The fish with hands ▶

Everyone knows that fish live in water, they move by swimming, and they use their fins and tail to help them move. But there's an exception to every rule and this is it. Named, appropriately, the handfish, these odd fish have fins which look like hands, and they use them to walk on the ocean floor. Four specimens of this ten centimetre-long species were seen near Tasmania, Australia. Handfish walk along the seabed eating small worms and other creatures. They move slowly and so must be an easy target for predators. However, researchers think they may have a secret weapon: a toxic skin that kills most attackers.

◀ 2 'Yoda' bat

This little bat became an Internet sensation because of its resemblance to the character of Yoda in the *Star Wars* films. The bat was discovered in Papua New Guinea, but so far it hasn't been named or officially classified. It's just one of over a hundred new species found on scientific surveys of Papua New Guinea this year. Scientists speculate that there could be many more undocumented species in the more remote mountains and forests of the area. The 'Yoda' bat is a fruit bat, with a diet of flowers and fruit, and may play an important role in the rain forest eco-system.

3 Is it a squid? Is it a worm? ▶

This nine centimetre-long marine animal was a big surprise to the researchers who first saw it. A remotely-operated underwater vehicle captured images of it at a depth of 2.8 kilometres in the sea around the Philippines. It looks like a squid because it has tentacles on its head. And it looks like a worm because its body is divided into segments. So the scientists, thinking it might be either a type of squid or a kind of worm, decided to name it squidworm. Closer examination shows it is indeed a worm and suggests it could belong to a new family of segmented worms, but the name of squidworm has stuck.

8b Easter Island

Listening Easter Island

1 You are going to listen to a commentary from a video about the Easter Island statues. Look at the pictures and find out what *moai* and *pukao* mean.

2 💿 **2.1** Listen to the commentary. Answer the questions.

1 How many statues exist?

2 What are they of?

3 What are the statues made of?

4 How were they made?

5 When were they made?

6 Do all of the statues have hats (*pukao*)?

3 💿 **2.1** Listen again. Are these sentences about the statues' hats (*pukao*) true (T) or false (F)?

1 The hats are painted red.

2 The hats have special significance.

3 The hats are made from the same rock as the main statues.

4 One theory is that the hats were carried to the statues.

Glossary

carbon-dating (n) /ˈkɑːbn deɪtɪŋ/ a method for finding out the age of old objects

ramp (n) /ræmp/ a slope that connects things which are at different levels

Easter Island is part of Polynesia and is a UNESCO World Heritage Site.

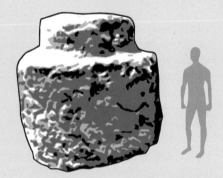

Pukao can be up to 2.5 metres high.

Easter Island statues or *moai*. The figure second from right wears a *pukao*.

Easter Island statues

Grammar speculation and deduction about the past

4 Read the sentences about the Easter Island statues. Choose the most logical option.

1 The Easter Islanders *can't have / must have* respected their ancestors.

2 It *might have / must have* taken months to carve a statue.

3 The Easter Islanders *can't have / may have* carved other objects as well.

4 They *couldn't have / must have* used dozens of men to move the statues.

5 The first Europeans to see the statues *might have / must have* been amazed.

5 Complete the conversations with the words.

can't have been	must have seen
may have seen	

A: This looks interesting. I like wildlife films.

B: Yes, it's just started. It looks really familiar, though. I ¹ _____ it before, I think.

A: Really? It says in the paper that it's a brand new series, so it ² _____ on before.

B: Oh? Well, I ³ _____ a trailer, then. I know it was advertised a lot.

can't have been	might have been
could have phoned	must have been
might have been	must have had

A: That's weird. I've got four missed calls on my phone.

B: Same number each time? It ⁴ _____ important if they called four times.

A: No, different numbers. But they didn't leave any messages, so it ⁵ _____ that important. I wonder how I missed them?

B: You ⁶ _____ your phone switched off.

A: No, I didn't.

B: Well, you ⁷ _____ busy or the volume ⁸ _____ down low or something.

A: Yes, Maybe. Well, I don't recognise the numbers, so I suppose they ⁹ _____ by mistake.

6 Pronunciation weak form of *have*

🔊 **2.2** Listen and repeat five of the sentences from Exercise 5.

Vocabulary history

7 How many ways can you complete these sentences? Use these words.

ancestors	ancient	beliefs	century
fragments	period	pieces	prehistoric
sacred	society	traditions	

1 That was an exciting … in history.

2 The Polynesians had strong … .

3 It's an interesting … monument.

4 The archaeologists found … of pottery.

5 We think these objects are from Polynesian … .

8 Dictation speculating

🔊 **2.3** Write the comments you hear. Then match them with the situations.

1 _____

2 _____

3 _____

4 _____

5 _____

a You can't get through to your friend's mobile phone.

b Your friends haven't arrived for your birthday party.

c Your sister's gone out. Her keys are on the table.

d The TV show you are watching seems familiar.

e Your boss is very late for a meeting.

8c Crop circles

Reading and listening crop circles

a crop circle

a wallaby

a poppy

poppy seed capsules

1 🔊 **2.4** Listen to a news story from Australia. What's the connection between the photos?

2 🔊 **2.4** Read the news story. Complete the article with these words. You can use the words as many times as you think necessary. Then listen again and check.

> extraterrestrial   hoaxers   humans   patterns
> physical   poppies   tools   wallabies

3 Read these comments that people made after hearing this news story. Which comments are supported by the information given in the story?

a   'Crop circles must be hoaxes because there is no other rational explanation.'
b   'Wallabies live in Australia, so they can't have made the UK crop circles.'
c   'I think the crop circles might have been the result of animal activity.'

4 All these words are in the news story. Which groups of words (a–c) can replace the words in bold in these sentences?

a	b	c
circular	explanation	bizarre
complex	suggestion	odd
geometric	view	weird

1   That's an interesting **theory**.
2   I've read about this **strange** phenomenon.
3   The building has an **intricate** shape.

A bizarre theory

The strange and fascinating phenomenon of crop circles – which actually aren't simply circular but form intricate geometric ¹ _patterns_ in farm fields – has inspired many possible explanations over the years. Crop-circle enthusiasts who prefer para-normal explanations for the circles believe that they must be messages left behind by ² _____ visitors, while more conventionally scientific-minded people have theorised that they might have resulted from natural ³ _____ forces, such as wind or heat. But now, there's another, even more bizarre explanation: ⁴ _____ .

As the BBC News and many other news outlets are reporting, Lara Giddings, Attorney General for the Australian state of Tasmania, told a Parliamentary hearing that ⁵ _____ have been eating ⁶ _____ in fields that provide legal opium for morphine and other painkillers. Apparently, according to Giddings, the ⁷ _____ are eating the ⁸ _____ and then becoming so disoriented that they run around in the fields erratically, creating paths that resemble crop circles.

An official with an Australian poppy-cultivation company told ABC News that in the process of consuming the poppy-seed capsules, the ⁹ _____ often also eat some of the substances that cause opium's hallucinogenic effect in ¹⁰ _____ . The weird suggestion that animals may have been the cause of Australian crop circles, however, doesn't really explain the crop-circle phenomenon. Are they capable of creating the sort of intricate geometric ¹¹ _____ seen in most crop circles? What about the crop circles found thousands of kilometres away from Australia, in the UK?

This odd explanation also doesn't account for the alternative view that crop circles are nothing more than elaborate jokes. A University of Oregon physicist, Richard Taylor, speculates that crop-circle ¹² _____ may now be using increasingly sophisticated ¹³ _____ such as GPS devices and laser pointers to burn complex ¹⁴ _____ into fields.

8d You must be joking!

Real life reacting to surprising news

1 Read the news stories. Do you think they are true or false?

1 More than a dozen scientists and yeti enthusiasts from Canada, Estonia, Sweden and the US flew to Siberia yesterday to exchange findings with their Russian counterparts at a day-long yeti conference.

2 One of the UK's most famous poets has written a book of poems about bees.

3 Representatives of the fishing industry warn that tuna is almost extinct.

4 The UK government has announced a new initiative to use decimal measures. From April 1 there will be ten hours in each day.

2 Complete the expressions for showing surprise with these words.

| having | joking | mistake | off | on | right |
| sure |

1 Come _____ it!
2 That can't be _____ !
3 They must have made a _____ .
4 You must be _____ !
5 You're _____ me _____ !
6 Are you _____ ?

3 **Pronunciation showing interest and disbelief**

2.5 Listen and repeat the expressions from Exercise 2. Pay attention to your intonation.

4 **Listen and respond reacting to surprising news**

2.6 Listen to the statements. Imagine a friend of yours is speaking. Respond with your own words. Then compare your response with the model answer that follows.

1
Look! It's snowing outside.

Are you sure?

8e In the news

Writing a news story

1 Writing skill structuring a news story

a Read the mixed-up notes (a–d) of a news story. Which section is the introductory sentence?

> **a** The area _____ (be) temporarily affected as the lightning _____ (cut off) electricity supplies. Later, the fire fighters _____ (say) the man was incredibly lucky.
>
> **b** The fire service _____ (respond) immediately to the call. According to the owner of the house, it all _____ (happen) extremely quickly.
>
> **c** An unbelievable *three* bolts of lightning _____ (strike) a house last night, but fortunately, nobody was hurt.
>
> **d** Neighbours _____ (call) the police and fire service after the first bolt of lightning _____ (start) a small fire.

b Write the story in the correct sequence and with the correct verb forms.

_____
_____
_____
_____
_____
_____

Vocabulary *-ly* adverbs in stories

2 Write the six *-ly* adverbs in the story next to the adverbs with similar meanings.

1 briefly: _____
2 instantly: _____
3 luckily: _____
4 really: _____
5 rapidly: _____
6 unbelievably: _____

3 Complete the sentences using adverbs from Exercise 2.

1 She spoke _____ slowly, but I still didn't understand.
2 _____ , it wasn't a serious accident.
3 I only saw them _____ .
4 It was _____ dangerous.
5 She replied to my email _____ .
6 The fire was _____ put out.

4 Grammar extra *-ly* adverbs

> **▶ -LY ADVERBS**
>
> We use *-ly* adverbs with:
> **1 main verbs**
> *The fire service responded immediately to the call.*
> **2 whole sentences or clauses**
> *Fortunately, nobody was hurt.*
> **3 adjectives**
> *The man was incredibly lucky.*
> **4 past participles of verbs**
> *The area was temporarily affected.*
> **5 other adverbs**
> *It all happened extremely quickly.*

Rewrite the sentences with the adverbs in brackets in the correct position. Make changes to punctuation as necessary.

1 nobody knows what happened (incredibly)
_____
2 this is not the first time this has happened (sadly)
_____
3 the car was damaged (deliberately)
_____
4 the man spoke about the incident (sadly)
_____
5 things are returning to normal (gradually)
_____
6 we were shocked by the news (incredibly)
_____

Wordbuilding noun → adjective

> ▶ **WORDBUILDING noun → adjective**
>
> We can make adjectives from nouns by changing the endings of the nouns.
> *mystery* + *-ous* → *mysterious*
> *religion* + *-ous* → *religious*
> *astronomy* + *-ical* → *astronomical*
> *ceremony* + *-al* → *ceremonial*

1 Make these nouns into adjectives with *-ous* and *-al* endings. Note that all except two need a small spelling change. All the adjectives are in Student's Book Units 1–8.

1 adventure: _____
2 ancestor: _____
3 archaeology: _____
4 benefit: _____
5 centre: _____
6 courage: _____
7 fact: _____
8 fame: _____
9 finance: _____
10 glamour: _____
11 globe: _____
12 history: _____
13 humour: _____
14 industry: _____
15 nature: _____
16 nutrition: _____
17 physics: _____

2 Complete the sentences with some of the adjectives from Exercise 1.

1 Apparently, ants are quite a _____ food source.

2 I'm not _____ at all: I'm even scared of ants.

3 I've been working on an _____ dig all summer. We're looking for evidence of an ancient civilisation.

4 It's a _____ report about the status of several endangered species.

5 The news has had a _____ impact and many countries are affected.

6 This species seems to do well in _____ areas, despite the pollution.

Learning skills using the Internet (2)

> Listening to the news on the Internet is one of the best ways of getting additional listening practice.

3 Here are some reasons why listening to the news is often easier than listening to other things. Match the sentence halves.

1 News stories are often international, so
2 News stories tend to follow a similar format, so
3 News items are often narratives, which
4 Websites tend to use the same speakers, so
5 News videos give you pictures

a you can get used to their voices and understand them better.
b to support the story you are listening to.
c you might have already heard some background information in your own language.
d tend to be easier to understand than opinion items.
e when you are familiar with this, you can concentrate on the actual language of the story.

4 You can use the same set of questions to help you understand any news story better. Can you complete these questions?

1 Where _____ ?
2 When _____ ?
3 Who _____ ?
4 What _____ ?
5 How _____ ?
6 Why _____ ?

5 🔊 2.7 Listen to two stories from different news websites. Make notes using the questions from Exercise 4. Is there enough information to answer all of the questions?

Check!

6 Write the names of the animals in the correct spaces. (Don't leave a space between the words if there are two.) The letters in the shaded squares spell another animal.

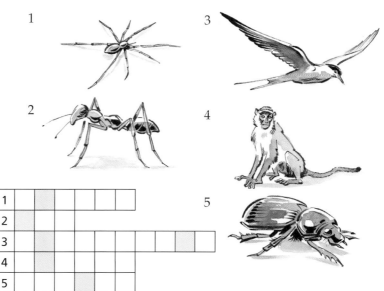

9a Electronic money

Vocabulary money

1 Write the words for these definitions.

1 a piece of paper to show you've paid for something: r_____

2 a piece of paper with the price you need to pay for something: b_____

3 coins and notes: c_____

4 information about money going into and out of your account:
b_____ s_____

5 something you can use instead of money:
d_____ c_____

6 a method of payment without cash or cards:
b_____ t_____

Reading and grammar noun phrases

2 Read the article about passwords. Answer the questions.

1 What kind of passwords are mentioned?

_____

2 What two characteristics should a password have?

_____

_____

3 Who is Mark Burnett?

_____

4 What is the list of codes with the article?

_____

3 Complete the article with these words. Write – if no word is necessary.

a	a	a	all	the	the	the	the	the
their	your	your	your	your	your			

Passwords

If you are one of 1_____ millions of people who use 2_____ online banking and 3_____ cash machines, then you will have 4_____ password. You might also use 5_____ password to access 6_____ email account, especially when you are not at 7_____ own computer. In theory, 8_____ password you use should be unique and secret. Security expert Mark Burnett says 9_____ these codes should be like personal secrets. But a lot of 10_____ people are not very good at keeping 11_____ passwords secret, and even more people are terrible at choosing 12_____ personalised password.

Look closely at 13_____ list of passwords shown here. These are 14_____ ten most commonly used passwords in 15_____ world. They seem to be very obvious and predictable, don't they? Is 16_____ password there? If you want 17_____ bank details and email to be secure, it might be time to choose 18_____ new one!

❶	123456
❷	password
❸	12345678
❹	1234
❺	-----*
❻	12345
❼	dragon
❽	qwerty
❾	696969
❿	mustang

* Not appropriate to publish in this book–too rude.

4 Grammar extra reflexive and reciprocal pronouns

> ▶ **REFLEXIVE and RECIPROCAL PRONOUNS**
>
> We use reflexive pronouns when the subject and object are the same:
> *I bought myself a CD.* (not *I bought me*) = the CD is for me
> *I bought him a CD.* = the CD is for someone else
>
> We use reflexive pronouns when we want to emphasise that the subject did something alone:
> *I did it myself.*
>
> We use the reciprocal pronoun *each other* when more than one person does the same thing:
> *They all looked at each other, waiting for someone to speak.*

a Choose the correct option.

1 We bumped into *each other / ourselves* in the supermarket.

2 Did you carry all those bags *each other / yourselves*? They look really heavy.

3 We like to treat *each other / ourselves* and go out for a meal once a month.

4 They sent *each other / themselves* a card on their birthdays.

5 When did you two first meet *each other / yourselves*?

6 They saved up and paid for everything *each other / themselves*.

b 🎧 2.8 Complete the sentences with a reflexive pronoun or *each other*. Then listen and check.

1 My dad made .... an egg sandwich.

2 I saw .... reflected in the shop window.

3 Sue and I phone .... every day.

4 She's got .... another beautiful outfit!

5 It's his own business, so he pays .... quite well.

6 They looked at .... across the table.

5 Pronunciation linking

a Write the word that comes before these words in Exercise 4b.

1 .... egg
2 .... in
3 I
4 .... outfit
5 .... own
6 .... at

b 🎧 2.8 Listen again and repeat the sentences.

Vocabulary *lend* or *borrow*?

6 Look at the example. Then complete the sentences with the correct form of *lend* or *borrow*.

Banks *lend* money to their customers. People *borrow* money from banks.

1 Never .... money to a stranger – you won't see either again.

2 Could I .... this book? I'll bring it back next week.

3 My friend .... me her bike for the weekend and someone stole it!

4 I can't afford to buy a new suit for the wedding. I wonder if my brother will .... me his?

5 Haven't you got an umbrella? You can .... mine if you like.

6 Where's my dictionary? I can't remember who I .... it to.

9b Gift items

Listening choosing a gift

1 🔊 **2.9** Listen to the conversation between two sisters who are choosing a gift for their aunt. Tick (✓) one or more options (a–c).

1 What do they look for on the Internet?
   a unusual presents
   b luxury gifts
   c special deals

2 What kind of jewellery does their aunt wear?
   a a gold chain
   b earrings
   c gold rings

3 What does the GoodWeave logo mean?
   a the carpets aren't made by children
   b the carpets aren't made in factories
   c the factories have been inspected

4 What kind of silk items do they consider?
   a kimonos
   b tablecloths
   c wall hangings

Glossary
hand-woven (adj) /hænd'wəʊvn/ describes a fabric or material that is made by hand
logo (n) /'ləʊgəʊ/ a picture or design that represents an organisation
wall hanging (n) /wɔːl 'hæŋɪŋ/ fabric with a design or picture that can go on the wall like a painting
weave (v) /wiːv/ to make threads into fabric

2 🔊 **2.9** Listen again. Match the gift ideas (a–c) with the sentences.

a pieces of jewellery
b rugs
c antique silk wall hangings.

1 These are no longer produced.
2 These are being made following traditional methods.
3 These can be made to your individual design.
4 These have been chosen for their quality.
5 These are imported from the people who make them.

Grammar passives

3 Read about each product and choose the correct option.

At this workshop in Kolkata, delicate gold necklaces for weddings ¹ *are assembling / are being assembled*. Each piece ² *contains / is contained* up to 45 grams of gold. According to the merchant, they ³ *will buy / will be bought* mostly for brides from low-income families.

In Azerbaijan, carpets ⁴ *have made / have been made* by hand for centuries. Both wool and silk ⁵ *use / are used*, and popular designs ⁶ *include / are included* birds, animals and scenes from daily life.

Vocabulary adjectives

4 Look at these descriptions. Underline the adjectives that give factual information. Circle the adjectives that give opinions. Which type of adjective comes first?

1   a lovely plain gold chain
2   beautiful traditional hand-woven rugs
3   gorgeous antique silk wall hangings
4   nice silver necklaces

5 Add these factual adjectives to the table.

19th century   blue   hand-made   Italian   large   mass-produced   old   plastic   tiny   wool

1	How big?	
2	How old?	antique
3	How is it made?	hand-woven
4	What colour?	
5	Where from?	Chinese
6	Material?	gold silk

Silk is a highly versatile and decorative textile. Because of its price, it [7] *has often associated / has often been associated* with luxury goods in both the East and the West. Nowadays, more and more synthetic materials [8] *are substituting / are being substituted* for silk.

6 Rewrite these sentences with the adjectives. Use the same order (1–6) as in the table.

1   The factory makes toys. (plastic / mass-produced)

2   It's a wall hanging. (silk / 19th century)

3   We bought a rug in the sale. (blue / wool)

4   She usually wears earrings. (gold / large)

5   It's a box. (Italian / tiny)

6   We've got some chairs in the garden. (plastic / old)

7 Dictation describing objects

2.10 Listen and write the information about an object. When you hear 'full stop', this means you have reached the end of a sentence. Then look at the photos and decide which object is being described.

1
2
3
4
5

9c Trade routes

Listening trade routes

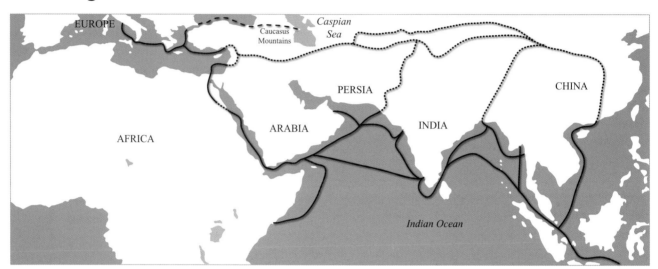

1 You are going to listen to a radio item about trade routes. Before you listen, find the following places on the map.

Arabia	China
Caspian Sea	Europe
Caucasus Mountains	India

2 🎧 **2.11** Listen to the radio item. Match the routes on the map (1–3) with their names (a–c).

1 .... a The BTK railway

2 – – – – – – – b The Silk Road

3 _____ c The Spice Route

black pepper   cinnamon

cardamom   ginger

Glossary
driving force (n) /ˈdraɪvɪŋ fɔːs/ the reason for or 'power' behind a change
echo (n) /ˈekəʊ/ a repetition of something, usually a sound

3 🎧 **2.11** Listen again. Write letters (a–c) for the route and draw arrows for the direction.

		Route a BTK b Silk Road c Spice Route	Direction East to West ◄— West to East —►
1	oil products		◄—
2	European goods	b	
3	precious stones		
4	glassware	b	
5	perfumes	b	
6	paper		
7	ceramics		
8	black pepper		

Word focus *much*

4 Look at two uses of *much* from the radio item. Then insert *much* in the correct position in the sentences.

Much of this epic railway has already been built. = *much + of* + noun (quantity)

The sea trade routes [...] became much more important. = *much* + comparative adjective (comparison)

1 How did it cost you?

2 I've spent far too money today.

3 This shirt is nicer.

4 How of this paper do you need?

5 She always uses too perfume, I think.

6 I haven't had time to go shopping recently.

7 Oh, that's too expensive!

8 I can get this cheaper online.

9d It's in the sale

Real life buying things

1 Read the first line of these exchanges between a customer (C) and a shop assistant (A). Write the responses in full using the words in brackets.

1 A: We have several models. Here are some of our most popular ones.

   C: _____ ?

   (look at / one)

2 C: How much is this one?

   A: _____ ?

   (sale)

3 A: Do you like this one?

   C: _____ .

   (want / more modern)

4 A: Is it for a gift?

   C: _____ .

   (yes / back / brother / not like)

5 A: Can I help you?

   C: _____ ?

   (work / dining room section)

6 C: I'm looking for a table I saw on your website.

   A: _____ ?

   (have / reference number)

7 A: We can deliver it within two days.

   C: _____ ?

   (how much / charge)

8 C: Do I pay the full amount now?

   A: _____ .

   (yes / card / cash)

Vocabulary shopping

2 Complete the sentences.

1 I can't get the printer today. They haven't got any i_____ s_____ .

2 All the t_____ are busy. We'll have to wait in the queue.

3 I bought this jumper, but it's the wrong size. Can I e_____ it for a smaller one?

4 They don't charge much for d_____ , but they only come to my area every two weeks.

5 I can't find it on the website without the r_____ n_____ .

6 Keep the r_____ – you might need it to r_____ the clock.

3 Pronunciation silent letters

🔊 **2.12** Say these words and cross out the silent letters. Then listen and check.

eighth	foreign	neighbours	sight
vehicle	whale		

4 Listen and respond shopping

🔊 **2.13** Listen to the shop assistant's questions. Respond with your own words. Then compare your response with the model answer that follows.

1

Can I help you at all?

No, thanks. I'm just looking.

9e For sale

Writing an advert

1 Writing skill relevant and irrelevant information

a Look at the photos of three items for sale on a second-hand goods website. Complete the table with the relevant information. Which two pieces of information are not relevant?

a

black	unwanted gift
chocolate brown leather	very comfortable
digital SLR camera	550 euros
four years old	3-seater
HD movie mode	26,000 km
Italian design	12 MP
metallic blue	4,500 euros
need payment quickly	3-door hatchback
our first purchase when married!	18–55 mm lens
petrol engine	

b

c

Item	Nissan Micra	Canon EOS	Leather sofa
Age		brand new	
Description/ Features			
Condition	regularly serviced		
Other information	economical fuel consumption	carrying case included	easy to keep clean
Price			400 euros

b Read the advert for item a. What additional information has the seller included?

2

Write adverts for items b and c. Use the information from Exercise 1a and add any other information you think necessary.

FOR SALE

FOUR-YEAR-OLD NISSAN MICRA. METALLIC BLUE, 3-DOOR HATCHBACK. IT HAS A PETROL ENGINE AND THE FUEL CONSUMPTION IS VERY ECONOMICAL. THE CAR HAS BEEN SERVICED REGULARLY AT NISSAN AUTHORISED GARAGES.

It has been used mainly at weekends and has only done 26,000 kilometres. It is in excellent condition. 4,500 euros. Please call evenings only, or email:

Wordbuilding compound adjectives

> ▶ WORDBUILDING compound adjectives
>
> Compound adjectives are made of two words often joined by a hyphen. They are usually adjective + adjective, adverb + adjective or noun + adjective combinations.
> *freshly squeezed orange juice*
> *world-famous market*

1 These compound adjectives appear on Student's Book page 110. Match them with the nouns they can describe.

1 world-famous:

2 sweet-smelling:

3 lethal-looking:

4 hand-dyed:

5 eight-year-old:

> actor   boy   brand   child
> flowers   knife   leather
> lemons   silk   street   weapon

2 Complete the compound adjectives in these sentences with these words. There is one extra word.

> hand   locally   newly   old
> paper   solar   vacuum

1 Online banking is a .... -free system.

2 ....-made shoes are very expensive.

3 We sell .... grown vegetables.

4 This ....- powered battery charger is really useful on long journeys.

5 This coffee stores well because it's ....-packed.

6 It's a nice coat, but it's a bit ....-fashioned.

Learning skills recording new words (2)

3 Look at the strategies (a–d). Write notes for these words. Which techniques work best for which words? Does it depend on whether the word is a verb, noun or adjective?

borrow: ....

merchant: ....

mass-produced: ....

a draw a picture of the word
b write other words connected to this word (opposites, synonyms, words it reminds you of, etc.)
c write where you might read, hear or use this word
d write a personalised sentence with the word

4 On Student's Book page 106, you wrote personalised sentences with words connected with money. Find six new words in Student's Book or Workbook Unit 9 and write personalised sentences with them.

....

....

....

....

....

Check!

5 Write the names of the things. Then use the second letter of *f* and the first letter of the other things to spell someone you would see in a shop.

a ....   c ....   e ....   g ....

b ....   d ....   f ....   h ....

	a	b	c	d	e	f	g	h
Letters								
Word								

Unit 10 No limits

10a Human limits

Reading what can the body take?

1 Read the information on *Human limits*. Write these section headings in the correct places.

Blood Loss	Dehydration	Hot Air
Body Heat	Diving Deep	Lack of Oxygen
Cold Water	High Altitude	Starvation

2 Read the information again. Answer the questions.

1 How long can we survive without food?

2 How long can we survive without water?

3 How long can we survive at 150°C?

4 At what percentage blood loss would we need a transfusion?

5 What's the maximum core body temperature we can withstand?

6 What helps people who live at high altitudes?

Grammar defining relative clauses

3 Complete the sentences with the information in sentences a–f and relative pronouns as necessary.

1 That's the patient

2 This is a new kidney

3 Cosmetic surgery is a medical procedure

4 I talked to the surgeon

5 That's the hospital

6 That was the day

a I came out of hospital then.
b I read about him.
c It can be expensive.
d It was grown in a laboratory.
e She operated on me.
f They do heart transplants there.

4 Pronunciation sentence stress

🔊 **2.14** Listen and repeat the sentences from Exercise 3.

5 Grammar extra non-defining relative clauses

> ▶ **NON-DEFINING RELATIVE CLAUSES**
>
> The information given in non-defining relative clauses is not essential to the meaning of the sentence. In non-defining relative clauses, you cannot replace *who* or *which* with *that* and you cannot leave out the relative pronoun.

Look at the example. Then write the information as one sentence. Write the information in the same order. Note the commas before and after the non-defining relative clause.

Example:
The hospital / opened last year / fantastic.
The hospital, which was opened last year, is fantastic.

1 This operation / performed frequently / not dangerous.

2 The nurse / explained everything to me / very professional.

3 The injection / nurse gives me / doesn't hurt.

4 My ankle / I broke last year / completely healed.

5 Our doctor / very young / very knowledgeable.

Vocabulary medicine

6 Choose the correct option (a–c).

1 donor
  a a person
  b a place
  c a procedure

2 scan
  a an illness
  b a place
  c a procedure

3 injection
  a a person
  b a cure
  c a procedure

4 radiographer
  a a person
  b a place
  c a treatment

5 stitches
  a an illness
  b a test
  c a procedure

6 ward
  a a person
  b a place
  c a treatment

Human limits

A 64-year-old woman fell on the ice last December. Her arthritis stopped her from getting up. She lay in the snow for hours. Her temperature dropped to 21°C. Her heart stopped. But doctors revived her and today she is fine. Medical science is always learning more about how much a body can take. Yet as Duke University physician Claude Piantadosi notes, 'At some point, it's impossible to rescue yourself.' Here's current thinking on the extremes of human endurance.

42°C
1

When core body temperature reaches 42°C, heatstroke can't be reversed and is fatal.

4,500 metres
4

Consciousness fades for most people. With bigger lungs and more red blood cells, highland dwellers are OK.

40%
7

You can survive after spilling 30 per cent. At 40 per cent, you'd need an immediate transfusion.

5°C
2

Water saps body heat. You'd last no more than 30 minutes in a 5°C sea. Life vests keep you up to slow heat loss.

86 metres
5

Without equipment, most folks black out before 2 minutes and below 18 metres. The best free diver made it to 86 metres.

45 days
8

Lose 30 per cent of body weight and death is imminent, though disease will probably kill you before you starve to death.

150°C
3

In a burning building or a deep mine, adults can withstand 10 minutes at 150°C.

11 minutes
6

Typically, you'd black out within 2 minutes. With training, people can hold their breath nearly 11 minutes.

7 days
9

Every cell needs water. Unless you replace the litre you lose daily, you won't last much more than a week.

10b A new life

Grammar second conditional

1 Complete the quiz questions with the correct form of the verbs. Then answer the questions for yourself.

How would you cope in a new life?

Take our quick quiz and see how you would do.

❶ If you _____ **(have to) move to somewhere new, where** _____ **(you / go)?**
a somewhere more urban than where you live now
b somewhere with a better climate than where you live now
c somewhere as similar as possible to where you live now

❷ Imagine you _____ **(take) only one bag with you. What** _____ **(be) in it?**
a not much – you'd rather get new stuff
b some practical stuff that might be useful
c family photos and videos

❸ What _____ **(you / miss) the most from your old life?**
a it's hard to say without knowing what the new life _____ (be) like
b the house you live in at the moment
c seeing your friends and spending time with them

❹ If you _____ **(move) to a new country, what** _____ **(be) the hardest thing to adapt to?**
a a new language
b the food
c the social customs

❺ Do you think you _____ **(find) a job easily if you** _____ **(go) to live somewhere new?**
a yes, you _____ (welcome) the chance to do something new
b yes, you _____ (probably / do) your type of work anywhere
c no, you _____ (have to) retrain as something new

❻ What _____ **(be) the best thing about living in a new place?**
a everything – you _____ (love) to change your life
b the chance to look at things differently
c nothing – if you _____ (have) no choice about moving

Answers

Mostly a: You're ready for new horizons! Are you unhappy where you are or do you just have itchy feet?

Mostly b: You're the kind of person who uses their head and looks at the pros and cons of a situation. You'd cope well in a new place.

Mostly c: You're a home bird, happy where you are or possibly a little unadventurous? It might not be wise to move somewhere new.

2 Choose the most logical option.

1 If I wanted to study in the UK, I *would / could / might* have to learn English.

2 I *wouldn't / couldn't / mightn't* imagine losing my job!

3 If I lost my job, I *would / could / might* be shocked.

4 If you spoke the language, you *would / could / might* ask for help.

5 I *would / could / might* love to move to the city – village life is a bit dull.

6 You never know – you *would / could / might* enjoy it if you tried it.

7 If you could spend a year travelling, where *would / could / might* you go?

8 If I went travelling for a year, there's a chance I *would / could / might* never come home!

3 Complete the conversation with the first and second conditional.

A: ¹ _____ (you / go) on one of those space tourism flights?

B: No! I ² _____ (be) terrified. I ³ _____ (not / go) if you ⁴ _____ (pay) me!

A: I think it sounds great. If the tickets ⁵ _____ (not / be) so expensive, I ⁶ _____ (love) to do that.

B: They ⁷ _____ (probably / get) cheaper in the future.

A: Yes. OK, if the price ⁸ _____ (drop) far enough, I ⁹ _____ (buy) us two tickets.

B: Far enough for you to afford? That ¹⁰ _____ (never / happen)!

Listening a different climate

4 🔊 **2.15** Listen to two colleagues discussing life in different climates. Which five of these ways of dealing with cold and hot climates do they mention?

active lifestyle	daily routine
air conditioning	fires
car technology	food
clothes	swimming pool

5 🔊 **2.15** Listen again. Complete the sentences with *man* and *woman*.

1 The _____ doesn't like going outside in really cold weather.

2 The _____ tends to eat a lot in a cold climate.

3 The _____ prefers hot places to cold places.

4 The _____ thinks a siesta in the middle of the day is a good idea.

5 The _____ doesn't like to sleep during the day.

6 The _____ is quite happy living where he/she is.

6 Complete these sentences using the second conditional. Who do you think said each one?

1 I _____ (not / enjoy) living in Canada.

2 I _____ (feel) cold even if I _____ (wear) high-tech clothes.

3 If I _____ (live) in Canada, I _____ (get) fat.

4 I think you _____ (avoid) the heat if you _____ (got up) early.

7 Dictation *if* …

🔊 **2.16** Listen and write the parts of the sentences. Then match parts 1–4 with parts a–d to make complete sentences.

1 _____

2 _____

3 _____

4 _____

a _____

b _____

c _____

d _____

10c A limitless brain?

Listening science in movies

1 Look at the photo. What do you think is happening? Choose one of the options (a–c).

a The weight of the man's brain is being calculated.

b The man's brain activity is being measured.

c Scientists are trying to read the man's mind.

2 🔊 **2.17** Listen to a radio programme about films and science. What's the connection between the film and the photo?

Glossary
neurologist (n) /njʊəˈrɒlədʒɪst/ a specialist in the nervous system and the brain

3 🔊 **2.17** Listen again to what the presenter says. Answer the questions.

1 What aspect of films do they look at in this radio programme?

2 What is the main idea of the film which is being discussed?

3 What does the main character of the film do?

4 What happens after he does this?

4 🔊 **2.17** Listen to what the guest says. Use the information you hear to complete the sentences.

1 It's not even .... that we only use 20 per cent of our brain.

2 We use different parts of the brain for different ....

3 There are no unused or .... regions of the brain.

4 It would be incredibly .... for the human body.

5 We actually already have .... brain power.

5 What does the presenter suggest about the things the film's character achieved?

Word focus *take*

6 Look at these extracts (1–3) from the radio programme. What do the words in bold mean? Match the extracts with the expressions (a–d). There is one extra expression.

1 The main character **takes** a special pill.

2 … if we knew how to **take advantage of** our brains properly …

3 **It doesn't take** a genius to achieve this.

a benefit from or use well

b consume food or drink

c carry something

d it's not necessary

7 Write the meaning of *take* in these sentences.

borrow	carry	have	invite	lead	react
steal	travel				

1 I'm taking my parents to the cinema tonight.

2 Someone's taken my umbrella!

3 Where are you taking me?

4 Is it OK if I take your car tomorrow?

5 If I were you, I'd take some food with you.

6 How did your brother take the bad news?

7 There are no buses. Let's take a taxi.

8 That's just what I was looking for. I'll take it.

8 Match the responses with the sentences in Exercise 7.

a As long as you take care of it.

b Great. We take credit cards or cash.

c He can't take it in, really.

d Here, take mine. I've got a hat.

e It's a surprise. It won't take long.

f It's OK. I can get a take-away.

g OK, but make sure it doesn't take the long way round.

h You'd better take enough money for drinks and snacks too.

10d First aid

Vocabulary injuries

1 What has happened in each case? Write sentences.

1 He _____

2 She _____

3 He _____

4 He _____

5 She _____

6 She _____

Real life talking about injuries

2 Match the comments (a–f) with the people (1–6) in Exercise 1. More than one answer is possible.

a I feel a bit sick.

b I've been stung.

c It hurts when I move it.

d It's just a sprain.

e It's nothing.

f It's really painful.

3 Look at picture 6 in Exercise 1. This is the conversation the person had with a friend just after the fall. Put the parts of the conversation in the correct order.

a A: Maybe. If I were you, I'd see the nurse.

b A: Really? It looks a bit swollen. What about this bit here?

c A: Well, you might have broken it.

d A: What have you done? Let me see!

e B: Do you think so?

f B: It doesn't hurt very much.

g B: Ow! Yes, OK, that's a bit painful.

4 Give advice to a friend. Choose endings to complete the sentences. Remember to use the correct verb forms.

get / looked at	keep / eye
get / X-ray	put / antihistamine cream
go / A&E	put / cream
go / see the doctor	wash
ignore	

1 If I were you, _____

2 You should _____

3 I would _____

4 I wouldn't _____

5 You'd better _____

6 Why don't you _____

7 It might be worth _____

8 You're best _____

9 Have you tried _____

5 Pronunciation *and*

2.18 What do you think is the correct order for each pair of words? Listen and repeat the sentences.

1 This is a _____ way to stop bleeding. (easy / quick)

2 Can you give me your _____ _____ ? (address / name)

3 We can help with all problems, _____ _____ . (big / small)

4 It's all written down in _____ _____ . (black / white)

5 The staff are _____ . (friendly / nice)

6 There's something for everyone, _____ _____ . (old / young)

6 Listen and respond advice

2.19 Listen to people say what has happened to them. Respond with some advice. Use your own words. Then compare your response with the model answer that follows.

1
I think I was bitten by a mosquito during the night.

Why don't you put some of this cream on?

10e What do you think?

Writing a personal email

1 Writing skill linking ideas

a Read the email. Cross out any options which are incorrect.

000

◀ ▶

Hi Jack

How are things? Here's something I need your help with. As you know, running is my main hobby. ¹ *However, / In fact, / To be honest,* you could say it's my only hobby. ² *Anyway, / All the same, / Well,* my running partner has decided to enter an ultramarathon next year. ³ *Actually, / Naturally, / Obviously,* he wants me to do it as well. He's very confident that we can do it.

⁴ *By the way, / Incidentally, / The thing is,* I am not convinced. What would you do? I know you aren't a runner, but ⁵ *all the same / even so / before I forget* you know me better than anyone.

I suppose I don't want to take the risk! It would be terrible to try and not make it! Anyway, I'd appreciate your thoughts.

Cheers

Ali

Send   **Cancel**

---

b What is Ali asking for advice about? Why does he ask Jack?

c Complete the sentences from Jack's reply with these words. There is more than one possible answer.

> anyway   by the way   even so   in fact
> incidentally   naturally   obviously   of course
> to be honest   well

1 I'm sorry it's taken me a while to reply to your email. I've been thinking about what you said, _____ !

2 _____ , I've never been faced with this kind of situation.

3 _____ , doing a race like that is going to be a massive challenge.

4 _____ , it's up to you in the end.

2 Rewrite these words from Jack's reply as full sentences.

1 I not know / what / I / do in your position.

2 Even so, if you / have / right training, you / do it.

3 As I understand it, you / do race next year if you / decide do it.

4 That / give you / plenty of time / to prepare and see if / a good idea.

5 I / sure / you / not regret it.

6 By the way, we / probably call in / visit you / next month / if we / go / Scotland.

3 Use the sentences from Exercises 1c and 2 and your own ideas to complete Jack's reply to Ali's email.

Hi Ali

_____

You are the only person who knows what your body is capable of. _____

It seems like a great opportunity, so if I was you I would seriously consider it. _____

I'll let you know a couple of days in advance. If you haven't made up your mind, we can talk about the ultramarathon a bit more then.

Regards

Jack

Wordbuilding suffixes *-ful, -less*

> ▶ **WORDBUILDING suffixes *-ful, -less***
>
> We can add *-ful* to the end of a noun to mean 'with' and *-less* to mean 'without'.
> a *painful* injection
> *limitless* expansion

1 Rewrite these words with *-ful* or *-less* to make adjectives from the Student's Book. Six of the words make common adjectives with both suffixes.

1 beauty: ....
2 breath: ....
3 care: ....
4 cheer: ....
5 colour: ....
6 grace: ....
7 harm: ....
8 life: ....
9 peace: ....
10 power: ....
11 resource: ....
12 respect: ....
13 stress: ....
14 success: ....
15 tune: ....
16 use: ....

2 Complete the sentences with words you wrote in Exercise 1.

1 Be .... You don't want to make a mistake.
2 He's a very .... dancer, despite being nearly two metres tall.
3 Modern life can be pretty .... , but we can learn to take it easy.
4 She's very .... She always finishes difficult tasks.
5 The snake is .... There's no need to be frightened of it.
6 This mobile is .... – the battery runs out really quickly.

Learning skills improving your speaking

If you don't get many opportunities to speak English, you might feel that you can't improve as much as you want to. However, recording yourself and comparing your speaking to models is a very effective way of developing your spoken English. You can record your voice in several ways.

3 Which of these things do you have access to?

a a mobile phone   c a video camera
b a computer   d a digital voice recorder

4 Here are some ideas of things you can record. Can you think of any more?

- record English speakers from DVDs, the radio or the Internet. Then repeat their words and record yourself.
- record dialogue and conversations. Then take one of the roles, and repeat and record yourself.
- try to speak spontaneously for one minute on a topic which interests you (you can use notes to speak from). Record yourself.
- get together with a friend who is learning English and record dialogues from your coursebook.

When you listen to yourself, concentrate on one aspect of your speaking at a time. Then record yourself again and try to improve that aspect. Listen to the recordings you made in Exercise 6 on page 81.

5 Tick (✓) the thing you could improve most.

- Intonation – is it like an English speaker or like your own mother tongue?
- Fluency – do you hesitate a lot? Do you pause in the wrong places?
- Do you stress the correct words in a sentence?
- Do you stress the correct part of words with several syllables?
- Pronunciation of vowel sounds – do they sound like your mother tongue?
- Pronunciation of other sounds, such as consonants at the end of words – are you 'eating' the wrong sounds?
- Vocabulary, grammar and structure – do you have all the words you need?

Check!

6 Look at the completed word puzzle. Write the clues.

1 ....
2 ....
3 ....
4 ....
5 ....
6 ....
7 ....

1						b	e	e
2					b	i	t	e
3				b	l	a	d	e
4			d	o	c	t	o	r
5		r	e	f	u	g	e	e
6	m	a	r	a	t	h	o	n
7	a	s	t	r	o	n	a	u	t

Unit 11 Connections

11a New media

Vocabulary news

1 Read the headlines. Decide which section of a newspaper the headlines are from. Choose one of the options.

1

Motor world in shock after tragedy

entertainment / sports pages

2

Ford to cut 4,500 jobs

business section / colour supplement

3

Pirates kidnap yacht crew in Indian Ocean

politics and society / world news

4

Hospitals 'need another 1,000 nurses'

national news / world news

5

Why we welcome changes to the education system

comment and analysis / sports pages

6

Last night's TV: The X Factor

comment and analysis / entertainment

7

Defence minister to resign

business section / politics and society

8

Unions in talks over strike action

features / front page

Listening WildlifeDirect

2 🎵 **2.20** Listen to a radio interview with Jo Makeba. Who are these people? Complete the sentences.

1 Richard Leakey ....

2 Paula Kahumbu ....

3 🎵 **2.20** Listen again. Choose the correct option (a–c).

1 The presenter said that ... .
  a wildlife success stories never made the headlines
  b wildlife issues didn't make headlines
  c wildlife stories were usually disaster stories

2 Jo Makeba said that ... .
  a we rely too much on traditional media
  b it's easy for people to reach a wide audience these days
  c we don't need traditional media any more

3 The presenter asked ... .
  a who was interested in wildlife projects
  b if the Internet affected wildlife projects
  c how the Internet affected wildlife projects

4 Jo Makeba said that WildlifeDirect was ... .
  a a way of sending money direct to projects
  b a wildlife programme that went out at lunchtime
  c a website that brought small projects together

5 Paula Kahumbu told Jo that Rosy the eagle ... .
  a was WildlifeDirect's first success story
  b could see again
  c was filmed raising his chicks

Glossary
cataract (n) /'kætərækt/ a condition of the eye which makes sight difficult
fund (v) /fʌnd/ to provide money for something
lurid (adj) /'ljʊərɪd/ sensational and shocking

4 How did WildlifeDirect followers help Rosy the eagle?

....

....

Paula Kahumbu

Grammar reported speech

5 Rewrite these quotes from the interview using reported speech.

1 'Good news never makes the headlines.'
The presenter said ....

2 'We can publish our own photos directly onto the Internet.'
Jo Makeba said ....

3 'And what exactly is WildlifeDirect?'
The presenter asked ....

4 'Richard set up WildlifeDirect.'
Jo Makeba said ....

5 'The website published Rosy's story.'
Paula Kahumbu said ....

6 'And can I see him on the WildlifeDirect site?'
The presenter asked ....

Rosy

6 Read your friend's words to you. Then complete your comments to them using reported speech.

1 'I don't watch the news.'
You said ....

2 'I know how to upload photos.'
You told me ....

3 'Have you seen this programme before?'
You asked me ....

4 'The documentary has just finished.'
You said ....

5 'I'll tell you when the news comes on.'
You said ....

6 'Can you help me download this video?'
You asked me ....

7 Dictation You said …

a    d

b    e

c    f

🎧 **2.21** Listen and write the comments. Then match the comments with the pictures (a–f).

1 ....
2 ....
3 ....
4 ....
5 ....
6 ....

11b Mobile technology

Reading innovations in communication

1 Read the article about the innovative system FrontlineSMS. Which paragraphs mention these things?

   a   two types of communications technology

   b   how FrontlineSMS works

   c   what's next for FrontlineSMS

   d   a connection between two systems

   e   an example of the system in action

   f   communications problems facing people in remote areas

   g   one way in which Ken Banks surprised people

2 Read the article again. Answer these questions in your own words.

   1   According to paragraph 1, what specific problem existed between phones and computers?

   2   How exactly did Ken Banks solve this problem?

   3   What's different about the way a laptop is used with FrontlineSMS?

   4   What kind of people or organisations use the system?

MOBILE TECHNOLOGY and the art of the possible

1 Have you ever wondered why you can't send a text message (SMS) from your laptop? Well, you can! For years, communications technology seemed to operate in two separate worlds. On the one hand, there was phone technology. Mobile (cell) phones could be used almost anywhere, as long as the phone signal had coverage. And in the early years of the 21st century, there weren't many places left outside the reach of a mobile phone network. On the other hand, there was the Internet. In contrast to phone networks, even today there are many places  in the world where you won't find a fast, reliable internet connection. But while phones could talk to phones, and computers could talk to computers, you couldn't send a simple text message between the two systems.

2 For people in richer countries, who had access to both systems, this may not have been a huge problem. But all over the world there are people in remote areas who have a huge need to share information simply and cheaply. Imagine you are a doctor about to set off on a tour of remote villages. You need a quick and simple way to tell the village health workers, pharmacists and others that you are on your way, and to find out what specific needs – medicines,

equipment – they have. The ideal solution would be to text your messages, using and storing the information on a computer. And that wasn't possible before a man called Ken Banks wrote the software that allows phones and computers to communicate with each other. Banks created the system, called FrontlineSMS, after returning from a trip to southern Africa. 'I wrote the software in five weeks at a kitchen table,' he says. 'I made it a generic communications platform that could be used for almost anything, and I made it free.'

3 Using FrontlineSMS requires simply a laptop computer and a mobile phone (even a fairly old or recycled one), and a cable. 'After downloading the free software online, you never need the Internet again,' Banks explains. 'Attach a mobile phone to the computer with a cable, type your message on the computer keyboard, select the people you want to send it to from a contact list the software lets you create, and hit *send*. Since it can run off an inexpensive laptop, it works for any organisation that wants to use text messaging, even in remote locations with unreliable electricity.'

4 One story of how FrontlineSMS works comes from Malawi. A rural healthcare network serving 250,000 people was revolutionised when a college student arrived with a hundred recycled phones and a laptop loaded with the software – saving a thousand hours of doctor time, thousands of dollars in fuel costs, and doubling the number of patients cared for.

5 Today FrontlineSMS delivers vital information in more than 50 countries and Banks is also launching a website through which concerned people in the developed world can donate text messages. But perhaps the most remarkable thing of all is that, having come up with such an innovative solution, Ken Banks didn't sell his idea to a huge multinational communications company. He simply gave it, free, to the people who could really benefit from it.

3 The article suggests there are several reasons why FrontlineSMS is so popular. What are they?

economical	long battery life
exclusive brand	reliable
freely available	simple
fun to use	sophisticated

4 Vocabulary extra communications technology

Complete the sentences with these words from the article.

cable	network
contact list	online
downloading	send a text message
internet connection	signal
keyboard	write software
launch a website	

1 If your mobile doesn't have a
   _____, you can't make calls.
2 The mobile phone _____ covers most places these days.
3 *Texting* means to _____.
4 If you want to use broadband, you need a fast and reliable _____.
5 Computer programmers are people who _____.
6 You need a _____ to connect devices unless you are using WiFi.
7 You can usually update programs by _____ them _____.
8 You need some kind of _____ if you want to type.
9 Most people store names and numbers in a _____.
10 If you want to reach a big audience, it's a good idea to _____.

Grammar reporting verbs

5 Write sentences reporting what was said.

1 'I'll find a solution.'
   (Ken Banks / promise)
   _____
2 'Would you like to tell us about your ideas?'
   (the company / Ken Banks / invite)
   _____
3 'We'll give all our customers ten free texts.'
   (the phone company / offer)
   _____
4 'Please donate text messages.'
   (the website / the public / ask)
   _____
5 'Don't be late for appointments.'
   (the doctor / the patients / tell)
   _____
6 'All hospitals should make arrangements for our visits next week.'
   (the officials / remind)
   _____

6 Complete the responses with the correct form of the verbs.

1 A: It's great that you can send texts with a computer now.
   B: I _____ (not / realise) you _____ (can / not).
2 A: I read his Twitter comments on my laptop.
   B: I _____ (not / know) Twitter _____ (work) on a laptop, just a phone.
3 A: You can't text if you haven't got a signal.
   B: Really? I _____ (think) you _____ (can).
4 A: I've sent everyone a text about the party.
   B: I _____ (wonder) if you _____ (send) a text or an email.

7 Pronunciation contrastive stress

 2.22 Listen and repeat the exchanges from Exercise 6.

11c Words and time

Listening old and new words

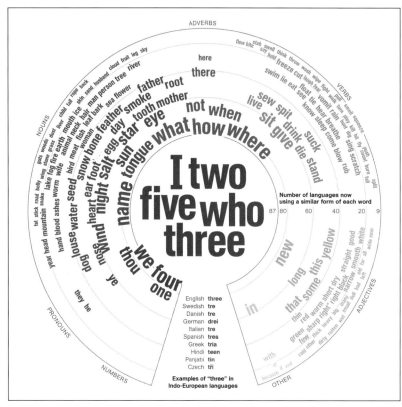

Examples of "three" in Indo-European languages

English	three
Swedish	tre
Danish	tre
German	drei
Italian	tre
Spanish	tres
Greek	tria
Hindi	teen
Panjabi	tin
Czech	tři

The English versions of two hundred words which have been used since the time of Mesopotamia. The words in the centre are the oldest and tend to be similar in different languages. The words near the edge are words that vary between languages and have changed more.

1 You are going to listen to a radio item about how words change over time. Before you listen, look at the diagram and answer the questions.

1 How do you say *three* in Hindi?

2 Which word has been in use longer: *three* or *here*?

3 How many languages today use a similar word for *who*?

2 2.23 Listen to the radio item. Find the words that are mentioned on the diagram.

Glossary
stable (adj) /'steɪbl/ unchanging

3 2.23 Listen again. Are the sentences true (T) or false (F)?

1 Researchers at Reading have been studying how global media will change language.

2 Mark Pagel looked at words that share a 9,000-year history.

3 Pagel analysed a group of 87 words.

4 The words that we use most frequently change the most.

5 Verbs and adjectives have changed more quickly than nouns over time.

4 What were two advantages of using a computer to analyse the data?

Word focus *time*

5 Look at these extracts (1–3) from the radio item. In which extracts do we use *time*:

a with an adjective?

b with a verb?

c as an uncountable noun?

1 How does language change over **time**?

2 … have not changed very much since **ancient times** …

3 The computer analysis, as well as **taking a lot less time** to look at the data …

6 Complete the sentences with these expressions with *time*. There is one extra expression.

difficult time	time
great time	time
have time	time and time again
modern times	take time
spend time	

1 _____'s up! Please stop writing now and hand in your answer sheets.

2 Thanks for everything. We had a _____ .

3 If you _____, could you phone your sister this evening?

4 Come on, it's _____ to get up.

5 It's a _____ for young unemployed people at the moment.

6 I've told you _____ not to leave the computer on.

7 I think we should _____ with our parents this weekend.

8 Are these ideas relevant in _____?

88

11d Can I take a message?

Real life telephone messages

1 Put the words in order. Then write A next to the four sentences from an answerphone message.

a message / this / Nils Davis / is / a / for

....

b Dan's / meeting / I'm / in /afraid / a

....

c delivery / it's / the / of / phone chargers / about

....

d 07956841 / my / Jill / I'm / name's / on / and

....

e take / I / message / can / a

.... ?

f calling / who's / yes,

.... ?

g later / you / I'll / try /call / and

....

h let / I'll / rang / know / you / him / that

....

2 The other four sentences in Exercise 1 are a receptionist's words in a phone conversation. Complete the conversation with four of the sentences (a–h) from Exercise 1.

C: Hello, can I speak to Dan, please?

R: ¹ ....

C: Oh, I'm returning his call.

R: ² ....

C: Yes, can you ask him to ring me?

R: ³ ....

C: It's Alice Black. My number's 07894524.

R: ⁴ ....

3 Pronunciation polite requests with *can* and *could*

a 🎵 **2.24** Can you think of more than one way to complete these requests? Listen and write what you hear.

1 Can .... call .... back?
2 Could .... ring .... later?
3 Could .... leave .... name?
4 Can .... give ....
.... number?
5 Can you tell .... I called?
6 Could you ask .... to phone me?

b 🎵 **2.24** Listen again and repeat the requests. Pay attention to your intonation.

4 Listen and respond making an appointment

🎵 **2.25** Listen to one half of a conversation between a patient and a doctor's receptionist. You are the receptionist. Respond with your own words using the word in brackets. Then compare your response with the model answer that follows.

1

> Can I speak to the doctor, please?

> I'm afraid the doctor is with a patient at the moment.

1 (patient)
2 (name)
3 (new)
4 (Friday)
5 (calling)

11e A community meeting

Writing a report of a meeting

1 Writing skill using notes to write a report

Look at these notes from a meeting about a street party. Then read the options (a–c) for each note. What do the notes mean? Cross out any options that aren't a logical explanation of the notes.

1	Present: 25
2	1 <u>party time & date</u>
3	30 April, 2 p.m. onwards. All agreed.
4	2 <u>preparations</u>
5	Music – Ms Clarke has contacted DJ.

1 a There were twenty-five residents at the meeting.
  b There will be twenty-five residents at the party.
  c Twenty-five residents came to the meeting.

2 a First, we discussed the time and the date of the meeting.
  b The first item on the agenda was the time and date.
  c The first thing we decided was the time and date of the party.

3 a It was agreed that the party would be on 30 April and would start at 2 p.m.
  b We agreed that the party will be on 30 April and will start at 2 p.m.
  c There was agreement that the party will start at two o'clock on 30 April.

4 a There are many things to be discussed.
  b The next thing to be discussed was the preparations.
  c The second item was the preparations.

5 a Ms Clarke offered to contact a local DJ about music.
  b Ms Clarke has some contacts with DJ music.
  c Ms Clarke said she had contacted a DJ about the music.

2 Grammar extra passive reporting structures

> ▶ PASSIVE REPORTING STRUCTURES
>
> We can use the passive with some reporting verbs to avoid repeating the same subject, or when the emphasis is on the reported words rather than the subject.
> *It was agreed that the party will be on 30 April.*
> *(= We all agreed that the party will be on 30 April.)*
>
> We can use this pattern with reporting verbs such as *agree, decide, explain, report, suggest.*

Rewrite the sentences using passive reporting structures.

1 Everyone agreed that the party would finish at midnight.

2 We decided that we would decorate the street.

3 Someone suggested that we should put up a marquee.

4 Some people explained that no special permission was needed for this type of event.

5 Someone reported that preparations were complete.

3 Use the full notes from the meeting about the street party and the ideas from Exercise 1 to write a report of the meeting.

<u>Street Party meeting 28 Feb</u>

Present: 25

<u>1 party time & date</u>
   30 April, 2 p.m. onwards. All agreed.

<u>2 preparations</u>
   Music – Ms Clarke has contacted DJ.
   Food – Ms Gregg to organise. Asked volunteers to sign list.
   Street decorations – Mr & Mrs Walker to organise. (lights, flags, balloons, etc.)

<u>3 questions</u>
   Mr Blair – will we need a licence? Mr Blair to check.

   Next meeting: 21 Mar, 8 p.m., community centre.

Wordbuilding prefix *un-*

> ▶ **WORDBUILDING prefix *un-***
>
> We can add *un-* to the beginning of a word to mean 'not'.
> *uncontacted* tribes
> *unseen* footage
> *unavailable* for comment

1 These words are all in the Student's Book. Which two are not adjectives?

> unable unbreakable unbroken
> uncomfortable uncooked unexpected
> unforgettable unfortunately unfriendly
> unhappy uninhabited unintentional
> unnecessary unpleasant unpleasantly
> unpredictable unsolved unspoilt
> unusual unwanted

2 Choose the correct option (a–c).

1 I don't think you should eat that if it's **raw**.
a unable b uncooked c unusual

2 I'm worried about Jack. His behaviour is **erratic**.
a unhappy b unpredictable c unsolved

3 They said they'd had a **nasty** experience at the hospital.
a unpleasant b unpredictable c unwanted

4 **Sadly**, these beautiful animals are endangered.
a unfortunately b unfriendly
c unpleasantly

5 The decision was quite **sudden** and we didn't know how to react.
a unable b unexpected c unspoilt

6 What was the most **memorable** experience of your trip?
a unbreakable b unforgettable
c unnecessary

7 It's a chain of **empty** islands in the middle of the Pacific Ocean.
a uncomfortable b uninhabited
c unnecessary

8 They said that if they had given offence, it was **not deliberate**.
a unbroken b unintentional
c unforgettable

Learning skills using the Internet (2)

3 Which of these things have you used the Internet for?
• reading the news
• reading something about your hobbies or interests
• reading something about your job or studies
• looking something up to get information about it

4 Have you done any of the things in Exercise 3 in English? Write down six key terms from your job, studies or interests. Can you say these words in English? Use the Internet to find out.

1 ....
2 ....
3 ....
4 ....
5 ....
6 ....

5 Which of these online resources would you use if you had these problems (1–5)? Write the online resource with the problem.

> dictionaries grammar practice practice exams
> translators vocabulary practice

1 How do you say *broadband* in my language?
....

2 Does the word *unconnected* exist in English?
....

3 I have to buy some computer gear, but I'm not sure what to ask for in English.
....

4 I'm still not sure how to report questions.
....

5 I'm thinking about doing a course to get an official certificate of my level of English.
....

Check!

6 Can you find eight words in the wordsquare? Use the clues to help you.

1 a kind of message you can send with your mobile
2 a way of sending short messages to unlimited numbers of people
3 computer code that runs programs
4 moving images or film
5 the 'title' of a newspaper article
6 up-to-date information
7 when a video is viewed thousands of times on the Internet
8 you need one of these or your mobile won't work

W	T	L	R	G	O	P	E	T	E
H	E	A	D	L	I	N	E	V	Y
C	X	R	F	I	N	E	N	I	S
I	T	S	O	F	T	W	A	R	E
P	W	U	O	P	Z	S	V	A	A
R	S	K	T	T	I	A	E	L	S
L	C	A	A	L	L	Q	R	G	L
T	S	I	G	N	A	L	T	D	C
Q	B	G	E	N	M	U	K	F	T
U	O	Y	T	W	I	T	T	E	R

12a A man of many talents

Reading a conflict in Cambodia

1 Read the article about Tuy Sereivathana. Match the extracts (a–e) with the gaps in the text (1–5).

a They were essential in the construction of the Angkor Wat temple and are depicted in honour on its walls.

b The origins of his role are found in the difficulties which faced Cambodia after decades of political turmoil.

c The success of his project is unprecedented:

d When farmers were arrested for clearing the forest, they could no longer feed their families.

e An early demonstration of his team's commitment to remote communities was their role in the creation of schools.

2 Read the article, including the extracts, again and find this information.

1 three reasons why the human–elephant conflict began

2 one example of the elephant's historic role in Cambodia

3 two problems that concerned farmers

A man of many talents

Tuy Sereivathana is a man with an unusual job title: Manager of the Human–Elephant Conflict Team for the Cambodian Elephant Conservation Group, for conservation group Fauna & Flora International. As a result of his expertise, not only the elephants but also 30,000 local people have benefited from the group's work. [1] _____

As masses of people relocated throughout Cambodia, they often created communities and farmland that affected elephant habitat. At the same time, with rain forests shrinking, hungry elephants come onto farmland, destroying crops. Desperately poor farmers fought back, killing elephants to protect their land and livelihood. As a result, Cambodia's elephant population, which numbered around 2,000 in 1995, crashed to several hundred. The action against the elephants was unexpected: they had been an integral part of Cambodia's traditions for centuries. [2] _____

To deal with the crisis, efforts at elephant conservation began. Given the historical status of the elephant, it was logical to expect progress in rekindling the connection between people and the environment. However, initial efforts didn't take the local people's needs into account sufficiently. Local people only associated wildlife protection with law enforcement. [3] _____ At this point, in 2003, Sereivathana became involved.

Day by day Sereivathana showed that he was concerned not only with elephants, but also with human beings. [4] _____ The government had still not established schools in these areas and farmers were very concerned that their children could not read or write. Sereivathana helped set up schools and attract teachers, and made wildlife conservation part of the curriculum. After gaining local trust, he launched a series of low-cost, highly ingenious strategies for keeping both crops and elephants safe. [5] _____ since 2005, not a single wild elephant has been killed in Cambodia due to human conflict.

3 Tick (✓) the option or options (a–c) which are correct.

1 Tuy Sereivathana is an expert in ... .
   a conservation
   b elephants
   c history

2 Sereivathana's project has benefited ... .
   a animals
   b local politicians
   c people

3 The article shows that Sereivathana ... .
   a is a good teacher
   b is effective in complex situations
   c understands the place of conservation

4 Sereivathana's success is the result of ... .
   a gaining people's trust
   b innovative ideas
   c spending lots of money

5 The number of Cambodian elephants today has ... .
   a increased greatly
   b reached previous levels
   c stopped declining

Grammar *should have* and *could have*

4 Write sentences with *should (not) have* or *could (not) have*.

1 Cambodia's elephants / die out / completely.

2 In theory, / the conflict between people and elephants / happen.

3 The Cambodians / build / Angkor Wat without using elephants.

4 Conservation efforts / re-establish / respect for elephants.

5 Conservationists / pay / more attention to human needs.

6 The government / provide / schools.

5 Write a response to each comment. Use *should (not) have* or *could (not) have*.

1   4

2   5

3   6

1 I failed my exam!

   (study harder)
2 I left my front door unlocked!

   (someone / break in)
3 My brother's got malaria.

   (take / tablets)
4 This shirt doesn't fit.

   (buy / bigger)
5 My sister has been a great help.

   (we / do / without)
6 We got lost on the way.

   (use / GPS)

6 Pronunciation *should have* and *could have*

🔊 **2.26** Listen and repeat the responses from Exercise 5.

12b What if ....?

Grammar third conditional

1 Match each beginning (1–5) with two endings (a–j). Then write the sentences in the third conditional.

1 If JK Rowling _____
   (not / write) the Harry Potter stories,

_____

2 If Tim Berners-Lee _____
   (not / invent) the Internet,

_____

3 If Alexander Fleming _____
   (not / discover) penicillin,

_____

4 If Dian Fossey _____
   (not / study) mountain gorillas,

_____

5 If Wangari Maathai _____
   (not / win) the Nobel Peace Prize,

_____

a   antibiotics (not / be) developed.
b   many people (not / hear) of her.
c   millions of boys (not / get into) books.
d   millions of people (die) from infections.
e   most of them (be) killed.
f   personal computers (not / become) so popular.
g   she (not / be) murdered.
h   she (not / become) a millionaire.
i   social networking (not / be) possible.
j   thousands of Kenyan women (not / have) an income.

2 Rewrite the pairs of sentences from Exercise 1. Use *if* in the middle of the sentences. You will need to change the position of some of the other words too.

1 _____

2 _____

3 _____

4 _____

5 _____

3 Rewrite the sentences using the third conditional.

1 JK Rowling didn't start writing until she became unemployed.
If _____

2 Tim Berners-Lee worked on hypertext because he wanted to share information with other researchers.
Tim _____

3 Alexander Fleming didn't clean his dishes and so penicillin grew on them.
If _____

4 Dian Fossey first went to Africa after a friend invited her on a safari.
Dian _____

5 After Wangari Maathai started the Green Belt movement, millions of trees were planted in Kenya.
If _____

Listening what if … ?

4 💿 **2.27** Listen to extracts from four conversations. Complete the notes.

	Who?	Topic?
1	two work colleagues	
2	two friends	
3	father and son	
4	two friends	

Glossary
authorities (n) /ɔːˈθɒrɪtiz/ official institutions or people in power
poacher (n) /ˈpəʊtʃə/ an illegal hunter
upset (v) /ʌpˈset/ to make someone unhappy or angry

5 💿 **2.27** Listen again. Choose the correct option (a–b) according to the information in the conversation.

1 If the man hadn't taken the tablets,
   a he wouldn't have got better.
   b he would feel better now.

2 If Fleming hadn't discovered penicillin,
   a nobody else would have discovered it.
   b some other scientist would have discovered it.

3 The actors in the Harry Potter films
   a haven't been in any other films.
   b would have appeared in other films.

4 The woman would have read the Harry Potter books
   a if she'd enjoyed them more.
   b if she hadn't been too old for them.

5 The father couldn't find the website because
   a he'd missed some of the characters.
   b he'd typed in too many characters.

6 The son told his father
   a he could have Googled the site.
   b he should have phoned him for help.

7 According to the film,
   a Dian Fossey was killed by poachers.
   b Dian Fossey and the poachers didn't get on.

8 Dian Fossey was
   a in favour of wildlife tourism.
   b against wildlife tourism.

6 Dictation Scott of the Antarctic

💿 **2.28** Listen and write the information about this photo, taken on Captain Scott's failed expedition to the South Pole in 1912. When you hear 'full stop', this means you have reached the end of a sentence.

1 _____

2 _____

3 _____

4 _____

5 _____

6 _____

12c Expert animals

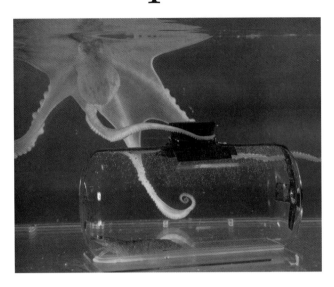

Listening expert animals

1 Look at the photo. What are the animals? Choose one of the options (a–c).

a   an octopus and a crab

b   a squid and a prawn

c   an octopus and a prawn

2 🔘 **2.29** Listen to a podcast about expert animals. Check your answers to Exercise 1. Make notes on the following information.

1   two examples of animals which are expert hunters

            ,

2   two examples of animals which are experts at camouflage

            ,

3   something the octopus does when a predator sees it

4   what happened to the prawn in the jar

5   what happened to the fish in a Seattle laboratory

6   how the Seattle laboratory staff discovered what had happened

Glossary

expertise (n) /ˌekspɜːˈtiːz/ the knowledge and skill that an expert has

ink (n) /ɪŋk/ dark liquid, named after writing ink, that some animals produce

lid (n) /lɪd/ a cover for a container

mimic (v) /ˈmɪmɪk/ to copy or imitate the appearance of something

squirt (v) /skwɜːt/ to quickly force a liquid out of a container

trail (n) /treɪl/ a line or path of marks on the ground or floor

Word focus *go*

3 Look at these extracts with *go* (1–3) from the podcast. Choose the correct meaning (a–c).

1   **going to** the other tanks
   a   disappear   b   leave   c   move

2   **going back** to its own tank
   a   belong   b   originate   c   return

3   what was **going on**
   a   continue   b   happen   c   talk

4 Complete the sentences with these words.

away   back   crazy   hungry   on   out
surfing   to

1   We live near the beach, so we go
            every weekend.

2   Sorry, I didn't mean to interrupt. Please go
            – I'm listening.

3   What a mess I've made! My boss will go
            when she sees this.

4   Do you ever go   zoos?

5   These traditions go   generations.

6   If we can't find any restaurants open, we'll have to go   .

7   Are you going   anywhere this summer?

8   I'm not going   tonight – there's a great film on TV.

5 Complete the sentences with these expressions.

go for a pizza	going for a coffee
go for a run	going for a walk
go for a swim	gone for lunch

1   I've got a headache. I'm   to get some fresh air.

2   'Is Jim there?' 'No, he's   . He'll be back in an hour.'

3   Do you fancy   after this?

4   When I'm training for the marathon, I   every morning.

5   I haven't got time to   today. The pool closes in twenty minutes.

6   'Are you doing anything special tonight?' 'I think we'll just   .'

12d I'm so sorry!

Real life making and accepting apologies

1 Complete the sentences with these words. Then write MA for making an apology and AA for accepting an apology.

accident	help	things	trouble

1 I couldn't .... it.
2 It's just one of those .... !
3 I'm really sorry you've gone to all this
....
4 Don't worry. It was an ....

2 Match the statements (1–6) with the responses (a–f).

1 You forgot to ring me!
2 There's no paper in the photocopier.
3 I'm so sorry. I haven't had time to get you a gift.
4 I'm sorry, but I think I left your umbrella on the bus.
5 We've run out of bread.
6 I can't believe I dropped that! I'm really sorry.

a Don't blame me. I don't do the shopping.
b Don't worry about it. It was just an old one.
c It's my fault. I forgot to refill it. I'll do it now.
d It's not your fault. It could have happened to anyone.
e Oh yes. Sorry about that!
f There's no need to apologise. It's not a problem.

3 Pronunciation sentence stress

🎧 **2.30** Listen and repeat the exchanges from Exercise 2. Pay attention to the words you stress.

4 Grammar extra *not only ... but also*

> ▶ **NOT ONLY ... BUT ALSO**
>
> We use the structure *not only ... but also* to add emphasis. The verb following *not only* is used with the auxiliary verb and the infinitive. The subject of the second verb goes between *but* and *also*.
> *Not only did he forget to buy the bread, but he also blamed me!*
> (= *He forgot to buy the bread. He blamed me.*)

Rewrite the sentences as one sentence. Use *not only ... but also*.

1 You forgot to ring me. You switched off your phone.
....

2 She lost my umbrella. She forgot to tell me.
....

3 He broke my vase. He didn't apologise.
....

4 They arrived late. They brought uninvited guests.
....

5 The octopus worked out how to get into the jar. It ate the prawn.
....

6 The scientist won the competition. She started a successful business.
....

5 Listen and respond making and accepting apologies

🎧 **2.31** Listen to each comment. Respond with your own words. Then compare your response with the model answer that follows.

1

> *You forgot to text me!*

> *Oh yes. Sorry about that!*

12e How to behave

Writing a website article

1 Writing skill revising

a Look at the underlined mistakes in these sentences. What types of mistakes are they? Write the type of mistake with the sentence.

> grammar   linking words   relevance
> spelling   style   vocabulary

1   Here are some <u>images</u> of my <u>travel</u> to Brazil.

2   My nephew is in Dublin this week. <u>My nephew</u> is learning English. <u>My nephew's</u> host family also speak Irish.

3   I've been to Lisbon several times, <u>therefore</u> I've never learned Portuguese.

4   If I hadn't learned Italian at school, I <u>had never gone</u> on holiday to Rome.

5   We used to go to Paris every year and stay with the same <u>familys</u>.

6   I went on a couple of homestays when I was a student. <u>I don't like flying</u>.

b Correct the underlined mistakes in sentences 1–5 from Exercise 1a.

1   ....

2   ....

3   ....

4   ....

5   ....

2 You are writing an article for a website which arranges host families for foreign language students in the United Kingdom. The purpose of the article is to give advice to families who want to be hosts. Read quickly through the sections (a–h) and decide which is the introduction to the article. Ignore the numbers in brackets for the moment.

a And finally, be patient with them when they speak English. If you never try to learn a language yourself, then you try taking a short course so that you know how it feels! (2)

b Find out if there is anything your student can't eat, either for religious reasons or because they really dislike a particular food item or plate. I don't like eggs, for example. (2)

c Make sure that you explain your household and family rules very clearly at the begginning. (1)

d Respect their privacy in spite of they are in your home. For the duration of their stay, their bedroom is there own private space. (2)

e Talk to your student about life in the student's own country. This helps you to anticipate what problems the student might have during the student's visit. (3)

f Treat the student as you would expect your own child to be treated if they are abroad. (1)

g We've had quite a few foreign students to stay since the last few years and each time it was been a different, but enjoyable, experience. If you're thinking about becoming a host family, here are a few tips for you. (2)

h You can ask your student to help with things as setting the table if that's what your own children do, but don't expect them to help you with the homework. (2)

3 Check each section using the criteria in Exercise 1. The number of mistakes in each section is given in brackets. Underline the mistakes.

4 Correct the mistakes and put the sections in a logical order. (More than one order is possible.) Write the finished article: *Tips for host families*.

Wordbuilding prefix *in-*

> ▶ **WORDBUILDING prefix *in-***
>
> We can add *in-* to the beginning of a word to mean 'not'.
> *inappropriate place*
> *inadequate [nets]*
> Sometimes the spelling changes to *im-* or *il,* depending on the first letter of the word.

1 Add *in-*, *im-* or *il-* to the beginning of these words.

1	accurate	9	logical
2	conclusive	10	offensive
3	credible	11	patient
4	effective	12	perfect
5	efficient	13	polite
6	expensive	14	possible
7	experienced	15	probable
8	legal	16	tolerant

2 Choose the correct option (a–c).

1 Let's buy this tent. It's pretty **cheap**.
   a inexpensive
   b inoffensive
   c intolerant

2 The hotel receptionist was **no good at his job**. He couldn't even find our room key!
   a inaccurate
   b inefficient
   c impossible

3 Jim's a great guy, but he's quite **new** at being a guide.
   a inexperienced
   b illogical
   c improbable

4 There is some evidence of elephants, but it's **not certain**.
   a inconclusive
   b inefficent
   c impossible

5 You should never be **rude** to your host.
   a illegal
   b impatience
   c impolite

6 I don't think you should drive at this speed! It's **against the law**!
   a ineffective
   b illegal
   c illogical

Learning skills dealing with exams

3 Try this quiz to see if you're an expert when it comes to exams. Tick (✓) the options (a–c) you think are correct.

1 What will help you get good marks in an exam?
   a knowing what format the exam takes
   b timing yourself for each question
   c revising vocabulary and grammar from the course

2 What should you do to prepare for an exam?
   a do some practice papers
   b go on holiday to an English-speaking country
   c look through your notebook

3 How should you behave in an exam?
   a try to finish as quickly as possible
   b leave time to check your answers before you hand the exam in
   c spend more time on the questions that have more marks

> **Answers**
> 1 All of these are good strategies.
> 2 Option b is not really necessary, although it might be a nice thing to do when your exams are over!
> 3 Option a is not a good idea at all! Use your time well.

Check!

4 Write the names of the things in the correct spaces. Only one word will fit into each set of spaces. (Don't leave a space between the words if there are two.) The letters in the shaded squares spell a kind of expert who would be useful on a field trip to see wildlife.

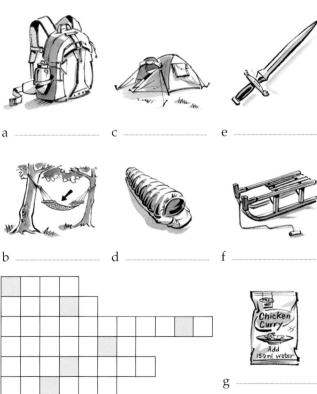

a .... c .... e ....

b .... d .... f ....

g ....

LISTENING TEST

SECTION 1

Questions 1 and 2

*Choose the correct letter, **A**, **B** or **C**.*

> **Example**
> At the college, Joanna saw
> (**A**) a leaflet about the festival.
> **B** a poster about the festival.
> **C** a DVD about the festival.

1 What did Joanna find on the festival website?
  A an online booking link
  B a full programme of events
  C information about student discounts

2 Joanna has already decided to book tickets for
  A a film.
  B a concert.
  C an exhibition.

Questions 3–10

Complete the notes below.

Write **NO MORE THAN TWO WORDS AND/OR A NUMBER** *for each answer.*

CITY ARTS FESTIVAL			
Dates	20th–30th **3**		
Telephone	**4**		
Sponsored by	**5**		
Day	Event	Venue	Price of student ticket
Monday	**6**	City Hall	£3.65
Wednesday	Jazz band	**7**	£2.50
Thursday	**8**	Library	£1.25
Friday	Modern Dance	College	**9** ....
Saturday	**10**	City Park	£1.50

SECTION 2

Questions 11–13

*Choose the correct letter, **A**, **B** or **C**.*

11 A free guided tour of the museum is available
   A at a fixed time every day it is open.
   B for up to twenty-five people each week.
   C if a minimum number of people make a booking.

12 Teachers bringing groups of school students have to
   A pay a fixed fee in advance.
   B complete an online booking form.
   C call first to arrange a convenient time.

13 For a short specialised tour, a group of college students would pay
   A £75.
   B £100.
   C £130.

Questions 14 and 15

*Choose **TWO** letters A–E.*

Which two facilities are available at the museum?
   A gift shop
   B tours in different languages
   C restaurant
   D room for hire
   E interactive displays

14 ....

15 ....

Questions 16–20

Complete the table below.

*Write **NO MORE THAN TWO WORDS AND/OR A NUMBER** for each answer.*

Year	Event	Result
16	Hunter comes to London	began work at anatomy school
1760	Hunter joins the **17**	began collecting animal specimens
1763	Hunter returns to London	began to work in private practice
1783	Hunter moves to Leicester Square	began what he called his **18** ....
1793	Hunter dies	**19** .... types of animal and plant in his collection
1799	Hunter's collection bought by **20**	still on show in London today

SECTION 3

Questions 21–23

Complete the sentences below.

Write **NO MORE THAN TWO WORDS** *for each answer.*

Sarah's proposal should begin with what's called a **21** .... of aims.

Sarah should prepare what's called an **22** .... for people taking part.

Sarah plans to use both people's opinions and **23** .... in her research.

Questions 24–27

What should Sarah include in her proposal?

> **A** an essential part of the proposal
> **B** a useful thing to include, but not essential
> **C** something which shouldn't be included in the proposal

*Write the correct letter **A**, **B** or **C** next to questions 24–27.*

24 how much it will cost

25 how participants will be chosen

26 how the results will be analysed

27 how the report will be presented

Questions 28–30

*Choose the correct letter, **A**, **B** or **C**.*

28 Sarah agrees to make sound recordings of
    A a random sample of interviews.
    B as many interviews as possible.
    C all the interviews she conducts.

29 Sarah will give her tutor updates
    A on a weekly basis.
    B after every twenty interviews.
    C when she runs into any problems.

30 What will Sarah promise participants?
    A not to put their names in her report
    B not to keep records of their answers
    C not to use the data for other purposes

SECTION 4

Questions 31–35

Complete the sentences below.

Write **NO MORE THAN THREE WORDS** *for each answer.*

CHRISTMAS ISLAND

Total size of the island: **31** .... square kilometres

Island's main industry: **32** ....

Species known to have become extinct:

  two types of rodent

  one type of **33** ....

Number of crab species living on the island: **34** ....

Name of group producing a report: **35** ....

Questions 36–40

Complete the sentences below.

Write **NO MORE THAN THREE WORDS** *for each answer.*

RED CRABS

Red crabs eat mostly **36** ....

Red crabs are described as **37** .... because each crab lives in a separate burrow.

Red crabs tend to stay in their burrows during the **38** .... season.

Red crab migrations are most likely in the month of **39** ....

To help migrating red crabs cross roads, **40** .... have been built.

READING TEST

SECTION 1

You should spend about 20 minutes on Questions 1–16, which are based on the two texts below.

How you are covered by the law when buying online
The law gives you rights when you buy goods or services without face-to-face contact.
It covers:
- online shopping
- television shopping, e.g. from shopping channels
- mail order shopping, e.g. from a catalogue
- shopping by phone and fax

The law says that:
- you must be given clear information about the goods or services before you buy
- you must get written confirmation of this information after you have made your purchase
- there is usually a 'cooling-off' period where you can cancel your order for any reason
- you can get a refund if items aren't delivered on the agreed delivery date
- If no delivery date is given, you can get a refund if items aren't delivered within 30 days of placing your order.

The usual rules that apply to shopping in person also apply to distance selling. So items must be:
- as described
- of satisfactory quality
- fit for purpose

Cooling-off period
If you buy something without face-to-face contact, you will usually have a 'cooling off' period of seven working days. It lets you cancel the order for any reason and get your money back. If you decide to cancel your order within the 'cooling off' period, you must tell the trader in writing. You don't have this cancellation right:
- when a new service starts immediately, e.g. paying for access to a website
- if the item is personalised or made to order
- if the item is perishable, e.g. food or flowers
- for publications such as the daily press and periodicals
- where the security seal has been broken on a CD, DVD or computer software
- if you buy something from an online auction like eBay – this is known as a private sale

Questions 1–10

Do the following statements agree with the information given in the text?

In boxes 1–10 on your answer sheet, write

> **TRUE**   *if the statement agrees with the information*
>
> **FALSE**   *if the statement contradicts the information*
>
> **NOT GIVEN**   *if there is no information on this*

1 The same law applies to things you buy on the phone and things you buy on the Internet.

2 The person who sells you something online should write to you about it.

3 You can ask for your money back if things you've bought online don't arrive on time.

4 The seller has to give a delivery date for things you buy online.

5 Different rules about the quality of products apply when you buy in person.

6 The 'cooling-off' period only applies to face-to-face purchases.

7 The length of the 'cooling off' period is normally fixed.

8 You need to have a good reason for cancelling an order in the 'cooling-off' period.

9 You must inform the seller of your reason for cancelling an order.

10 The 'cooling-off' period applies to fresh goods and newspapers.

Questions 11–16.

The text on page 106 has six sections, **A–F**.

*Choose the correct heading for sections **A–F** from the list of headings below.*

Write the correct number (i–ix) in boxes 11–16 on your answer sheet.

List of Headings

i   When will the payment be taken?

ii   What if I get charged for something I didn't order?

iii   Do I have to send things back?

iv   What if I have damaged the packaging?

v   What if I saw the goods in a shop, then bought them on the shop's website?

vi   Who pays for sending things back?

vii   What happens if you don't have a credit card?

viii   Can I get my money back?

ix   What if I need to try things out?

---

11 Section **A**

12 Section **B**

13 Section **C**

14 Section **D**

15 Section **E**

16 Section **F**

Buying things online: the 'cooling off' period

A Under the distance selling regulations, you are quite within your rights to change your mind at any time, return the goods and get a full refund including any delivery charges you have paid. This must happen within 30 days from cancellation, whether or not the goods have been sent back. Any related credit agreements will also cease to exist.

B You may be required to bear the cost of returning the goods, but only if this was made clear when you agreed to buy them. If the goods are faulty, then under the separate Sale of Goods laws, the supplier will always be responsible for the cost of returning them.

C In all other cases, your only obligations are to make the goods available for collection and to take reasonable care of them while they are in your possession. This is called a duty of care, and it lasts for a period of twenty-one days. Where you have agreed to return the goods, your duty of care continues until you do this and could be for as long as six months.

D Under a distance selling contract, a supplier cannot make refunds subject to the goods being returned unopened in their original packaging. One of the principles of the distance selling regulations is to give you a chance to examine the goods at home, not having had a chance to do so in the shop. It would be impossible for you to do this without opening the box or bag and making sure it's what you wanted.

E Also, you need to ensure that things are of good quality and work properly. Having said this, you will still be under a duty to take reasonable care of the goods while in your possession, and may be subject to certain instructions such as not to wear shoes outdoors, or remove hygiene seals.

F However, for goods and services paid for specifically in a distance selling context, you are automatically protected against fraudulent use of your payment card – whether this is a credit or debit card. So if you see that you have paid for goods you didn't buy, you can ask the card company for the money back.

SECTION 2

You should spend about 20 minutes on Questions 17–27, which are based on the text below.

An Archaeological Discovery in Australia

To the archaeologists, the site by the Jordan River, on the outskirts of present-day Hobart, capital of the Australian island state of Tasmania, did not look particularly promising. But when they began digging, they uncovered an extraordinary treasure trove: millions of artefacts, representing the oldest evidence of human habitation in the southern hemisphere.

For more than 40,000 years, the river bank was an important meeting place for Tasmanian Aboriginal people, who converged on a broad floodplain to trade goods and hold ceremonies. The spot was still being used as late as 1828, twenty-five years after Europeans first colonised the island. 'It has the potential to give us a glimpse into an unknown part of world history and the spread of Homo sapiens across the Earth,' said Rob Paton, who led the dig.

The dig was ordered after Aboriginal groups voiced concerns about plans to construct a bridge across the Jordan, as part of a new four-lane highway. Archaeologists were astounded by what came to light. Although Dr Paton's report describes the site as being of 'extremely high scientific significance', the Tasmanian government is resisting pressure to reroute the bypass road, claiming that the bridge will not destroy or disturb it. Opponents, however, point to concrete pylons which will be sunk into the grassy flood plain and plans to create a massive infill of rocks.

While the site is of international significance, it has particular meaning for Tasmanian Aborigines, whose heritage and history were virtually wiped out during the process of European settlement. Much of the Jordan valley was home to Aboriginal people, and three major tribal groups congregated regularly on the flood plain through the millennia: wild cherries were the main thing to be gathered in the area, which also offered plentiful river life as well as abundant kangaroos and wallabies for meat.

Michael Mansell, legal director of the Tasmanian Aboriginal Centre, said: 'That's a place that really strikes at our heart, and is about our identity, our past and our future. When you stand down by that levee, you can feel the presence of our ancestors, of the old people and the children.' Archaeologists say the site could rewrite Aboriginal history in Tasmania and Australia.

Digging eight test pits, they found 1,440 artefacts – including tools and spear tips – and concluded that three million objects lie buried. 'They're stone artefacts, they're used for day-to-day living, cutting and sharpening,' Dr Paton said. 'It's that day-to-day stuff that really is rarely found. To get a snapshot of what life was like 40,000 years ago is quite unique, not just for Australia but for hunter-gatherer sites anywhere in the world.'

With approval for the bridge expected to be granted soon, conservationists and Aboriginal groups have appealed to the federal government to intervene. One local politician has called for the site to be National Heritage listed.

Across the island, little trace remains of ancient indigenous culture. Coastal rubbish pits date back only 5,000–6,000 years, and inland caves were occupied about 14,000 years ago. Consequently, the riverbank site, where an estimated 300–400 people are believed to have converged regularly, is a real find.

Questions 17–20

*Choose the correct letter, **A, B, C** or **D**.*

Write your answers in boxes 17–20 on your answer sheet.

17 How did the archaeologists feel at the beginning of the dig?
   A excited to have located the site
   B optimistic about the likely results
   C unimpressed by the appearance of the site
   D unsure how long it would take to find anything

18 What is significant about the results of the dig?
   A how many objects were unearthed
   B what the age of the objects tells us
   C what the type of objects found suggests
   D the fact that similar objects are still in use

19 The dig took place because
   A the archaeologists thought the site might soon be damaged.
   B the local government wanted to change the route of a road.
   C local people were worried about a construction project.
   D Dr Paton was determined to lead it himself.

20 There is debate about whether
   A the site has real scientific significance.
   B the new road will really damage the site.
   C the use of concrete pylons is really necessary.
   D the local rock will support a large road bridge.

Questions 21–25

Complete the sentences below.

*Choose **NO MORE THAN TWO WORDS** from the passage for each answer.*

Write your answers in boxes 21–25 on your answer sheet.

Most of the objects found were made from **21** ....

As well as hunting and fishing, Aboriginal peoples used to pick **22** .... for food.

A total of **23** .... objects has been dug up so far.

Tools used for **24** .... and keeping things sharp have been found.

It has been suggested that the site be listed as having **25** .... status.

Questions 26–27

What has been found elsewhere in Tasmania?

*Write the correct two letters **A–E** in boxes 26–27 on your answer sheet.*
   A things that were thrown away by ancient people
   B places where ancient people lived
   C places where ancient people met
   D structures which ancient people built
   E places where ancient people dumped things

26 ....

27 ....

SECTION 3

You should spend about 20 minutes on Questions 28–40, which are based on the text below.

Even in his nineties, the German mountaineer Anderl Heckmair was still a popular guest at climbing events around the world. He would sit with a twinkle in his eye as young climbers introduced themselves, eager to shake hands with the man who led the first ascent of the north face of the mountain called The Eiger.

Heckmair had seen it all. His brilliant 1938 climb with three companions up the Eiger, notorious for its rock falls and sudden, violent storms, is still regarded as one of the greatest expressions of mountaineering skill in history. Reinhold Messner, perhaps the most celebrated living climber, thought the three-day ascent 'a work of art'.

Quite what Heckmair would have made of Dani Arnold is another question. In April 2011, Arnold climbed Heckmair's route in just 2 hours 28 minutes, a jaw-dropping record that stunned the Alpine climbing scene. The scale of Arnold's effort, two years in the planning, is mind-boggling. The psychological pressure on such a gloomy mountain wall, passing landmarks such as 'Death Bivouac' is obvious. A lot has changed since 1938, but the Eiger is still a dangerous place – even for a roped climber. Yet, for speed, Arnold climbed without anything to catch him if he fell. One loose handhold or falling stone and he would be dead – but he had to push such thoughts from his mind. 'I didn't even think for a moment about falling,' he says.

Apart from the danger, the athletic demands were huge. The north face itself is a gigantic amphitheatre, 1,600 metres in vertical height. Working every day as a guide in the mountains, the 27-year-old says he didn't need to do any special training. He had climbed the route several times so knew its secrets. The real challenge was getting his head right for the intense concentration required – he turned back on a couple of earlier attempts because he didn't feel right.

But Arnold's Eiger ascent wasn't the only mind-blowing speed ascent that year. A few months later in August, 22-year-old Andreas Steindl sprinted up the nearby Matterhorn in just 2 hours 57 minutes, starting at Zollhaus, on the outskirts of Zermatt in Switzerland. That's a vertical gain of 2,915 metres, and while the Matterhorn's Hornli Ridge, first climbed by Edward Whymper in 1865, is a much easier proposition than the Eiger's north face, the distance involved is much further.

Most climbers attempting the Matterhorn take the cable car to Schwarzsee, a pretty tarn lake at 2,500 metres much visited by hikers, and then walk a further two hours to the Hornli mountain hut at the foot of the mountain. After a night there, they continue at around 4.30 a.m., with the climb itself taking most parties another six to eight hours. Steindl left Zermatt at 4.05 a.m., using running shoes and ski poles approaching the peak, before switching to boots and crampons. He was on the summit just after 7 a.m.

Putting the mountain off-limits to other members of the public wasn't an option, so Steindl had to overtake about 90 other climbers on his way to the top, not easy on a steep mountain that claims a dozen lives each year, although he said he was buoyed by their words of support. Arnold faced the same problem on the Eiger, passing 20 roped parties, including fellow guide Simon Anthamatten and his client. Anthamatten was the previous record holder on the Matterhorn. Arnold's most anxious moments came while passing some climbers at the end of the so-called 'Traverse of the Gods', which leads back into the centre of the face, just before the final difficult section. 'Having all of those people on the route also had advantages,' Arnold says. 'They'd made a good path and most of the holds were free of snow. The disadvantages of course were that I'd sometimes have to wait maybe one or two minutes to pass.' That suggests it might be possible to go even faster, although Arnold says he is finished setting records on the Eiger.

Despite his youth, Steindl is not just a fast climber but a top skier and trail runner too, reflecting the narrowing gap between mountaineering and mountain racing, or 'skyrunning'. Zermatt isn't just famous for the Matterhorn but hosts two of the most prestigious cross-country mountain races in the world: the legendary Patrouille des Glaciers – a high-altitude ski-mountaineering event held in April – and July's Zermatt marathon. One of the team that holds the record for the Patrouille's 53-kilometre course is Florent Troillet, who, along with Anthamatten, held the Matterhorn record until Steindl's effort this summer.

Catalonian skier and ultra-running legend Kilian Jornet, three-time winner of the Ultra-Trail Mont Blanc race, has also shown an interest in speed ascents. He holds the record for the fastest ascent of Kilimanjaro, reaching the summit of Africa's highest peak in 5 hours 22 minutes in 2010. Jornet makes no secret of his admiration for the Italian mountain runner Bruno Brunod. In 1995, Brunod ran from Cervinia, on the Italian side of the Matterhorn, to the summit and back in just 3 hours 14 minutes, a record that really has stood the test of time and one that Jornet would love to add to his tally.

Are climbers in danger of turning the mountains into a race track? 'Climbers have always compared the speed of their ascents,' says Ueli Steck, who held the north face of the Eiger record until Arnold's climb. And though the speed and style of climbing has been transformed, the danger isn't much less than it was in Heckmair's day. 'The more you do it,' says Steck, 'the more things can go wrong.'

Questions 28–34

Complete the table below.

Choose NO MORE THAN THREE WORDS AND/OR A NUMBER from the text for each answer.

Write your answers in boxes 28–34 on your answer sheet.

YEAR	NAME OF MOUNTAIN	NAME OF CLIMBER	SPEED OF CLIMB
28	Eiger (north face)	Anderl Heckmair	**29** ....
1865	Matterhorn	**30**	unknown
1995	Matterhorn	**31**	3 hours 14 minutes
2010	**32**	Kilian Journet	5 hours 22 minutes
2011	Eiger (north face)	Dani Arnold	**33** ....
34	Matterhorn	Andreas Steindl	2 hours 57 minutes

Questions 35–40

Do the following statements agree with the information given in the text?

In boxes 35–40 on your answer sheet, write

TRUE	*if the statement agrees with the information*
FALSE	*if the statement contradicts the information*
NOT GIVEN	*if there is no information on this*

35 Heckmair climbed the north face of the Eiger alone.

36 Arnold climbed the Eiger without the usual safety equipment.

37 Steindl made sure no other climbers were about on the day of his record-breaking climb.

38 Simon Anthamatten felt sad when Steindl passed him on the mountain.

39 Florent Troillet still holds one climbing record.

40 Ueli Steck thinks climbing is safer now than it was in the nineteenth century.

WRITING TEST

TASK 1

You should spend about 20 minutes on this task.

You rent a furnished apartment from a property company. The washing machine has stopped working. You contacted the company a week ago, but it has still not been repaired.

Write a letter to the company. In your letter
- *explain who you are and why you are writing.*
- *say how the problem is affecting you.*
- *say what you want the company to do.*

Write at least 150 words.

You do not need to write any addresses.

Begin your letter like this:

Dear Sir or Madam,

TASK 2

You should spend about 40 minutes on this task.

Write about this topic.

Students should be taught to read and write using a computer, as handwriting will not be used in the future.

To what extent do you agree or disagree?

Give reasons for your answer and include any relevant examples from your own knowledge or experience.

Write at least 250 words.

HOW TO MARK THE WRITING TEST

TASK 1

There are four criteria for marking the Part One tasks, which are equally weighted.

Task achievement

This is an assessment of how well the student has fulfilled the task.

A successful task will:
- include at least the minimum number of words
- have a text structure appropriate to a letter
- be relevant to the context established in the input material
- achieve the writer's intended purpose
- cover the functions indicated in the bullet points

Coherence and cohesion

This is an assessment of how clear and fluent the writing is.

A successful task will:
- be appropriately organised
- successfully link information and ideas
- contain logical sequencing
- make effective use of cohesive devices

Lexical resource

This is an assessment of the use of vocabulary.

A successful task will:
- include a range of relevant vocabulary
- use vocabulary accurately
- use vocabulary in an appropriate way

Grammatical resource

This is an assessment of the use of grammar.

A successful task will:
- use an appropriate range of grammatical forms at sentence level
- use grammatical forms accurately

TASK 2

There are four criteria for marking the Part Two tasks, which are equally weighted.

Task response

This is an assessment of how well the student has responded to the task.

A successful task will:
- make clear the writer's position on the issues raised in a question or statement
- develop arguments to support that position
- support the arguments with evidence and examples
- include at least the minimum number of words

Coherence and cohesion

This is an assessment of how clear and fluent the writing is.

A successful task will:
- be appropriately organised
- successfully link information and ideas
- contain logical sequencing
- make effective use of cohesive devices

Lexical resource

This is an assessment of the use of vocabulary.

A successful task will:
- include a range of relevant vocabulary
- use vocabulary accurately
- use vocabulary in an appropriate way

Grammatical resource

This is an assessment of the use of grammar.

A successful task will:
- use an appropriate range of grammatical forms at sentence level
- use grammatical forms accurately

SPEAKING TEST

PART 1 – INTRODUCTION AND INTERVIEW

Let's talk about how you spend your free time.
- What do you do when you want to relax?
- Do you enjoy playing games / chatting online? Why (not)?
- Do you like to spend your free time alone or with other people (and why)?
- Has the way you spend your free time changed as you've got older?

PART 2 – INDIVIDUAL LONG TURN

Candidate Task Card

Describe a website that you enjoy using.
You should say:
    which website you use
    why you started using it
    what you use it for
and explain why you enjoy using it.

You will have to talk about the topic for one to two minutes.

You will have one minute to think about what you are going to say.

You can make some notes to help you if you wish.

Rounding off questions
- Do many people use this website?
- Are there other websites you use frequently?

PART 3 – TWO-WAY DISCUSSION

Let's consider first of all watching television.
- How popular is television in your country?
- Which type of programmes are the most popular (and why)?
- Do you think there is too much advertising on television?

Finally, let's talk about the television news.
- Do you think television is the best way to keep up with the news? Why (not)?

HOW TO MARK THE SPEAKING TEST

The speaking test is an assessment of how effectively students can communicate in English.

There are four criteria for marking the Speaking Test, which are equally weighted.

Fluency and coherence

This is the ability to:
- talk at a consistently normal speed
- link ideas and language together in logical sequences
- use the language features which create coherent, connected speech

Lexical resource

This is the ability to:
- use a range of relevant vocabulary
- use words appropriately to convey meaning
- use paraphrase strategies when required

Grammatical range and accuracy

This is the ability to:
- use a range of grammatical forms appropriately
- use grammatical forms accurately

Pronunciation

This is the ability to:
- use a range of phonological features to convey meaning
- produce intelligible individual sounds
- use stress, rhythm and intonation effectively

Audioscripts

Unit 1

🔘 **1.1**

What colour hair have you got? Is it your natural colour or do you use hair dye? Hair dye is big business. In the United States, people spend over a hundred million dollars every year just on red hair dye. It seems that a lot of us like red. But natural redheads aren't very common – they belong to a minority. Only about two per cent of the world's population have red hair. Red hair comes from northern Europe originally and in Scotland two out of five people possess the gene for red hair. This means that thirteen per cent of Scots are redheads. The gene also means your body is better at making vitamin D from sunlight – obviously a useful ability in northern lands. On the other hand, some redheads feel the cold more and are more sensitive to pain!

You need two copies of the gene – one from each of your parents – to get red hair and that's why natural redheads are disappearing. The world is changing and people are changing too. Young people often move away from their home areas to work or to study and end up staying away. So the chances of two red-hair gene carriers actually meeting is getting smaller. Now some scientists are speculating that by the year 2100 true redheads will be extinct.

🔘 **1.2**

1 Do you taste the words you hear?
2 Have words got colour for you?
3 Can you read without tasting words?
4 Which senses do you mix up?

🔘 **1.3**

P = presenter, G = guest
P: With me in the studio this afternoon is someone who experiences the world in a different way to most of us. Is that right, Holly?
G: Yes, I suppose it is.
P: Thanks very much for coming to talk to us.
G: Hi. It's a pleasure.
P: Now, Holly is colour blind and she's going to explain a bit about what that means …
G: Yes, that's right. I have red–green colour blindness, which is actually the most common kind. It's something you're born with.
P: So how common is colour blindness, exactly?
G: It is quite common – about ten per cent of men have some kind of colour blindness. On the other hand, it's rare in women – so I'm quite unusual, I suppose.
P: But what does it actually mean to be colour blind? What do you see? Or not see?
G: If you have red–green colour blindness, like me, it basically means that you can't tell the difference between shades of red and shades of green. They look more or less the same to me. So, for example, I can't tell if the DVD player is on or off.
P: Yes, of course, I see. And there are lots of electrical things which have red and green indicators.
G: Yes, although they are starting to make things with blue indicator lights for 'on' – which is much better for people like me.
P: And do we know what causes colour blindness?
G: Oh yes. It's a problem with the cells in our eyes. Our eyes normally see colour using three different kinds of cells. So one kind of cell sees red, another kind sees green and the third kind sees blue. But if you haven't got enough of one kind of cell, then this leads to colour blindness.
P: Is there a cure for colour blindness?
G: Well, an optician can give you coloured glasses or contact lenses, but they aren't very much help – at least not for me.
P: So can colour-blind people lead normal lives? You mentioned problems with electrical things …
G: I think that most of the time you can lead a normal life, as long as you don't want to be a police officer or an airline pilot – there are a few jobs you just can't do.

🔘 **1.6**

G = Grace Larsen, A = Alberto Costa
1 G: Hello, how are you? My name's Grace Larsen.
   A: I'm very pleased to meet you. I'm Alberto Costa.
2 B: I work in marketing. What about you?
   C: I'm in IT, actually.
3 D: I'm the manager of Pink cosmetics.
   E: Oh yes, I know that company very well.
4 F: I'm looking for a new job at the moment, actually.
   I: Are you? What kind of thing are you looking for?
5 J: How about meeting again?
   K: Yes, let me give you my card.

Unit 2

🔘 **1.8**

R = Robin, J = Judy
R: Have you heard of this guy, Philippe Petit?
J: No, I don't think so. Who is he?
R: He does these amazing walks on tightropes …
J: Like a circus performer? I'm not keen on circuses – I don't enjoy watching animals perform.
R: No, he's not in a circus or anything. He's a high-wire artist. He's done some absolutely incredible things.
J: What kind of thing do you mean?
R: Walking across a wire between the twin towers of the World Trade Centre, for example – look at this photo.
J: Wow! When was that, though?
R: In 1974, just after they were built.
J: I wonder why he wanted to do that?
R: Perhaps he just loves being high up!
J: But just looking at the photo is making me nervous! I can't imagine standing on a wire in the middle of … nothing! How wide is the wire?
R: I don't know. Does it matter? Even if it's a metre wide, there's nothing to hold on to!
J: And how high up was he in this picture?
R: It says here 417 metres.
J: That's crazy! He was lucky not to fall off.
R: I don't think it was luck. It's total skill and dedication. He's done dozens of walks. He started in Paris in 1971 and then he kept going. He's been across the towers of Notre Dame and the Sydney Harbour Bridge as well. But this twin towers walk is the most famous because it was completely illegal. The newspapers called it 'the artistic crime of the century'. He decided to do it in 1968 when they were still constructing the towers. Planning everything took six years.
J: Six years?
R: Yeah. And then, when he did it, he didn't just walk across from one tower to the other. He was on the wire for 45 minutes – he went back and forwards eight times! Eight! And when people noticed him, he started dancing.
J: Unbelievable!

🔘 **1.9**

1 Performing in public makes me nervous.
2 I enjoy being in the spotlight.
3 I've never given a speech in my life.

4　Going to dances is a good way of meeting people.
5　Telling jokes is quite hard to do.
6　I've been on stage a couple of times.

🎵 1.10
The experimental film *Life in a day* is quite unusual – in fact it's possibly unique. It gives us a picture of life in our world – the whole world – on one single day: 24 July 2010. The film is a documentary – not a drama or a thriller or a romantic comedy. But at the same time, it has moments of drama and of romance. In fact, the film is simply a lot of moments – 90 minutes of moments from people's lives around the world on that 24 July. Some of these moments are connected, some aren't. At times during these 90 minutes, it's difficult to concentrate, to be honest. Watching it becomes almost exhausting. So many images flash in front of your eyes. But the idea of the film is certainly interesting. The film itself is made from videos shot by ordinary people. There are no actors or professional film-makers or special effects. And although there is no story, there are themes: love, fear, hope, and so on.

The project began when film director Kevin Macdonald had an idea: 'to take the temperature of the planet on a single day', as he puts it. He sent about 400 cameras to 40 countries and asked people three questions: 'What do you love? What do you fear? What have you got in your pocket?' Then people used the cameras to film their lives, or the lives of those around them, and sent the footage back to Macdonald. And the astonishing thing was that the project grew to be much bigger than 400 people with cameras. A week after the 'day', Macdonald and his team had 4,500 hours of footage in 81,000 video clips from 192 countries. Even more astonishing, perhaps, was the fact that at that stage, Macdonald didn't have a plan for his film. He wanted to see all the footage first and try to choose 90 minutes from that.

So, what did he choose? What kind of picture do we get? There are women in Ghana singing while they work, an English student having a drink with his dad, men in India gossiping, market sellers in the Philippines having lunch … the list goes on. And there are words to go with the images too. The faces speak to us, telling us that they 'love football' or 'are afraid of growing up'. The film has been pretty successful – perhaps more than Macdonald expected. If you've missed it in the cinema, you can watch it on YouTube. It's an interesting way to spend an hour and a half.

🎵 1.12
1　Q:　Do you fancy going to the theatre on Friday night?
　　R:　Yeah, why not?
2　Q:　Do you want to go out tonight?
　　R:　Yes, sure.
3　Q:　There's a circus in town. Do you like the sound of that?
　　R:　It doesn't really appeal to me.
4　Q:　What did you think of the film?
　　R:　It was absolutely brilliant.
5　Q:　Did you enjoy the performance?
　　R:　To be honest, I was really bored.
6　Q:　What was the concert like?
　　R:　It was the best concert I've ever been to.

Unit 3

🎵 1.13
1　I got a great photo.
2　I knew it was a good idea.
3　They flew to London on Friday.

4　We dealt with the situation immediately.
5　I put on my snorkel.
6　We swam all day.
7　They saw a great white shark.
8　I fell in the water.

🎵 1.14
Hurricanes are giant, wet and windy tropical storms. They bring winds of over 250 kilometres an hour and the hurricane clouds can carry enough water for more than nine trillion litres of rainfall in a day. Now, if you're thinking that you don't know the difference between hurricanes, cyclones and typhoons, don't worry. They are actually the same thing. The different names just come from the different parts of the world – cyclones start in the Indian Ocean and typhoons in the western Pacific Ocean. Hurricanes begin in the Atlantic Ocean and there is an annual season from mid-August to late October.

One of the wettest and most destructive hurricanes in recent history was Hurricane Mitch. It hit the Caribbean and Central America in November 1998. By the time Mitch reached the coast, most people had already left the area. When the danger had passed and people had returned home, they couldn't believe what had happened. In Honduras, farmland had turned into desert. Bridges and roads had disappeared. Rivers had changed course. As Mitch passed over Honduras, so much rain fell that some rivers flooded to six times their normal size. In one day, the area had the equivalent of 200 days of rainfall. In places where there had been rivers with lines of trees, now there was nothing. The trees had all washed away. This kind of thing is not so unusual during hurricanes, but the power of Mitch was extreme. The tremendous winds had picked up sand and carried it for many kilometres before dropping it in a new area. Suddenly, there was a desert where people had had farms. Mitch had completely changed the land and, of course, the lives of the people who lived there. It took them many years to recover.

And although there will be hurricanes in the future as powerful as Mitch, the World Meteorological Organisation decided the name Mitch will never be used again.

🎵 1.15
a　Both men are now in hospital.
b　The men had fallen out of their boat.
c　Their families had called the Coast Guard
d　Coast Guards rescued two men from the sea this weekend.
e　because the men hadn't returned from a fishing trip.

🎵 1.16
I = interviewer, P = Pauline
I:　Now, you may remember seeing the name Bundanoon in the news headlines a while ago. Bundanoon is a small town near Sydney, Australia. It has its own supply of water from an underground water reserve. Some years ago, the residents of the town discovered that a water company had applied for permission to extract this water, bottle it, and sell it as drinking water. We spoke to Bundanoon resident Pauline Tiller earlier this week, about what happened next. Pauline, why didn't you want this water company to go ahead with their plans?
P:　Basically, because we were drinking the water in our homes, direct from our taps. We didn't want to buy bottled water – especially when it was already our own town's water supply!
I:　And how did you get involved in the story?

P: Well, I was using an old newspaper to mop up a water leak one morning when something in the paper caught my attention. I stopped and read this astonishing letter Huw Kingston had written about banning bottled water.

I: Huw Kingston is a local businessman in Bundanoon, is that right?

P: Yes, he had come up with this revolutionary idea – he wanted the town to fight the water company. And he also wanted us to ban bottled water completely! As soon as I read his letter, I knew that was the answer!

I: And what did you do next?

P: A few residents got together to investigate how we could go 'bottled water free'. At that time, we didn't know we were pioneers! While we were looking for information, we heard about another Australian town that had gone 'plastic bag free'. This really encouraged and inspired us. Then we found out that the carbon footprint of bottled water is 300 times greater than tap water! It became obvious that bottled water is a crazy idea. So we had a town meeting to discuss the whole thing and the town decided to become 'bottled water free'.

I: And I believe journalists from a national newspaper arrived while you were holding the meeting?

P: Yes, a lot of national and international newspapers had heard about our story. After they wrote about us, we got a lot of support from environmental movements. And in September 2009, we became the first 'bottled water free' town in Australia.

I: So you banned bottled water. But now, what do people – visitors to the town, for example – do if they want to get a drink of water?

P: All the water in our town is free, so you can get it from the tap. And if you want to take some water with you, our shops sell our own 'Bundanoon' reusable bottles.

🎵 1.17
1 We were fishing on the lake.
2 I was trying to bring the fish in.
3 He was shouting at me.
4 We were sitting in the boat.

🎵 1.18
1 Q: Did I ever tell you about the time we ran out of petrol?
    R: No. Where were you going?
2 S: I remember when I broke my leg.
    R: When did that happen?
3 S: I almost had a car accident last night.
    R: Really? What happened?
4 S: A couple of months ago, I decided to leave my job.
    R: Oh? Why?
5 S: You'll never believe who we saw in town at the weekend!
    R: Oh? Who was it?
6 Q: Did I tell you what I was doing when you phoned?
    R: No. What were you doing?

Unit 4

🎵 1.19
1 I look at my new son and I wonder about his future. The world will be a very different place in a few years' time, I'm sure of that. I want his life to be better than mine, but I worry that it might not be. There are some things I'm sure about: he'll learn to use a computer before he goes to school and he won't leave school at sixteen like I did. But everything is changing so quickly – it's really hard to say what his life will be like.

2 I think my baby will have a great life. Robots and computers will take care of all the routine, boring things like shopping, housework and stuff, so she'll have lots

of time to enjoy herself. She'll probably drive an electric car and live in a house that recycles everything. She might work from home, but she definitely won't work full time like I do. It'll be great!

3 My baby will definitely live longer than me. She'll probably live to be a hundred – that's what they say about babies born today. Will she be healthy? I think so – there are so many advances in medicine these days. I think they'll certainly find cures for many of the health problems we face today. So she might get ill at some point in her life, but they'll be able to cure her.

4 When I think about my children's future, the thing that worries me most is the situation with the environment – things like climate change and the oil running out really concern me. This could affect their world in ways we haven't imagined. It seems that my kids will probably speak Chinese – at least that's what people keep telling me! They may not learn it at school, but they'll need it for work and business, I reckon. So that could be a challenge!

🎵 1.20
1 People won't get ill in the future.
2 School students may study from home.
3 Climate change could affect everybody.
4 People will probably travel less in the future.
5 People might work until the age of 75.
6 English will probably be the only language you need.

🎵 1.21
1 It's ten miles from here.
2 Send me an email.
3 I'll see you soon.
4 I hope I don't fail this exam.
5 There's no oil in this jar.
6 How do you feel?

🎵 1.22
P = presenter, I = interviewer, A = Anton, C = Carey
P: Well, that's about all for today, but in our next programme, to celebrate the fact that it's 21 years since the birth of the world wide web, we'll meet some of the 'Internet generation' – people who were born at the same time as the Internet. We'll find out what it means to be 21 today and if it's so different from past generations. What's life like for this generation and how do they view what's ahead? Here's a little taste of next week's programme …

A: I don't believe in making plans. Plans are for old people. I like to be spontaneous.

I: So, marriage … a family …. a home of your own?

A: Yeah, when I'm older! Say … thirty-something. First, I'm going to enjoy myself.

I: You don't want to settle down, then? But you have a good job.

A: Oh yeah, work is fine, and I'll probably be promoted soon. I work hard, earn a good salary. And I like to spend it!

I: So Carey, what are you planning now that you've graduated?

C: Well, in July we have my graduation ceremony, my 21st birthday and my parents' 25th wedding anniversary in the same week, so that's going to be amazing. We're all really looking forward to that. Then after that, my main aim is to get a full-time job – because at the moment I'm still in the part-time job I've had since I was at school.

I: Is that a worry?

C: A worry? No. Something will come along, for sure. I'll try anything … I believe you have to go through life with an open mind, or you might miss an opportunity.

P: That was the voice of Carey, who in fact was in a car accident at 16 and has been in a wheelchair ever since. And before that you heard Anton, a young man who has also had some challenges in his life. Just two of the people you can hear more from in next week's programme, *Turning 21*, which will explore the hopes and dreams of the Internet generation. We hope you can join us then. And we hope you will be inspired, like we were, by what you hear.

🎵 1.23

1 a We'll meet some of the 'Internet generation'.
  b We meet some of the 'Internet generation'.
2 a We find out what it means to be 21 today.
  b We'll find out what it means to be 21 today.
3 a We have my graduation ceremony.
  b We'll have my graduation ceremony.
4 a I'll try anything.
  b I try anything.

🎵 1.24

1 Q: Are you going to fill in the form?
  A: Yes, I am.
2 Q: Will you be OK?
  A: Yes, I'm sure I will.
3 Q: Does she speak English?
  A: Yes, I think she does.
4 Q: Will they phone you today?
  A: No, I don't think they will.

🎵 1.25

1 Q: Are you looking for a new job at the moment?
  R: Yes, I am actually.
2 Q: Can you help me fill in this application form?
  R: Yes, sure.
3 Q: Do you mind if I give your name as a referee?
  R: No, of course not.
4 Q: Have you finished your CV yet?
  R: Yes, I think so.
5 Q: Could you show me how to upload my CV?
  R: Sure, no problem.
6 Q: Can you come to an interview next week?
  R: Yes, of course.

Unit 5

🎵 1.27

1 = Presenter 1, 2 = Presenter 2

1: Belinda, you've got some holiday destinations with a glamorous feel for us today?
2: Yeah, we've been looking at some of the best holiday spots for film fanatics. You've seen the movie, now have the holiday!
1: Where's your first recommendation?
2: First up, Monument Valley, home of a thousand westerns. When you drive into Monument Valley, you really do feel you're stepping onto the set of a cowboy movie. Film directors have been making westerns here since the 1930s and the huge red sandstone rock formations have provided the scenery to movies as different as *Stagecoach*, in 1939, and *Thelma and Louise*, in 1991.
1: It's in Texas, isn't it?
2: No, actually it covers an area of Arizona and Utah – in fact it's part of the Navajo Nation and Navajo families have lived there for generations. It looks quite remote, but it's easy to get to.
1: And what can you do there?
2: Well, much of Monument Valley is protected land, so if you want to take a tour, the best way is to go with a Navajo guide. I've been on a tour, and while it was spectacular, it was also pretty uncomfortable.

1: An authentic 'western' experience, then?
2: I suppose so. But a trip to Monument Valley is all about the scenery and so I think an even better idea is to take a hot-air balloon trip over the valley. A local business there has been running these tours every summer for a few years now. That's the way to go!
1: And from the emptiness of Arizona to somewhere completely different – Prague.
2: Oh yes. Now, since Hollywood 'discovered' Prague in the 1990s, this beautiful and vibrant city has been attracting a lot of action heroes – Tom Cruise was there to film *Mission Impossible*, and Wesley Snipes chased vampires through the Old Town in *Blade II*.
1: It's a very atmospheric city.
2: Yes, and of course Prague has always been one of Europe's main cultural centres, so there's a lot to see – museums, castles, fantastic architecture. In the last few years, airlines have been adding more flights and more connections, so it's really easy to get there.
1: OK, so I think we've just got time for one more recommendation.
2: I'll be quick! How about a walking tour in the romantic setting of films like *Notting Hill*, *Shakespeare in Love* and *Bridget Jones*? Yes, it's London – but seen from a different angle.
1: And for the kids, don't forget King's Cross Station, where they filmed one of the Harry Potter films. You can find more details of all these on our website …

🎵 1.28

1 How long was your last holiday?
2 How long did it take to get to your destination?
3 How long have you been in this class?
4 How long have you been learning English?
5 How long have you worked for your employer?
6 How long have you spent on this unit?

🎵 1.29

P = presenter, G = guest, S = Suzanne (caller), M = Marco (caller), J = James (caller)

P: OK, our lines are now open, so please phone us with your travel queries. Our studio guest this morning is Andrew Marshall, an expert in eco-tourism, low-impact travel, conservation issues and all things green. He's here to answer your questions. And our first caller is Suzanne … with a question about flying, I think. Hello?
S: Hi, yes, I've been hearing a lot about flying and climate change recently – about how much fuel planes use and the effect on the environment. But when I flew back from holiday last week, the in-flight magazine said that flying is greener than driving. So what's the truth?
G: Hi, Suzanne. Yes, some of the budget airlines have been making these claims. It's all about numbers and statistics – it's easy to use statistics in this way. But I think the best thing is to use your common sense. If you have a choice between flying and taking a train, for example, then the train is a much greener option. Flying is simply not eco-friendly.
P: And our next caller is Marco.
M: Hi, well, my parents want to go on an eco-friendly cruise. They've been going on cruises for about four years now, ever since they retired, but they've started to worry about conservation issues. Where can we get information about eco-friendly cruises?
G: Hello, Marco. Well, it's great to hear that your parents are thinking about the impact of their travelling. I should say first that many of the larger tour operators have been taking steps to improve things in this area. I think an internet search is the best place to start. I've seen quite a few green cruises advertised. Your parents can email the companies with any specific questions they have.

P: And James has a specific question about Madagascar.

J: Yes, I've always wanted to go to Madagascar, but the thing is, there are a lot of problems with threatened habitats and species there. I don't want to be part of the problem – should I think about a different destination?

G: Hi, James. You don't need to choose a different destination. There are quite a few local communities in Madagascar that have been working with international organisations to develop eco-tourism. You can join in with conservation projects or simply be a 'tourist' without having a negative impact.

P: Andrew, before we take the next call, let me ask you a bit more about Madagascar.

1.31

1 Q: Is anything wrong?
   R: Yes, I've lost my passport.
2 Q: I wonder if you could help us?
   R: Yes, of course. What's the problem?
3 Q: I'm sorry. Have you been waiting long?
   R: Yes, we've been here for ages.
4 Q: Is there anything you can do about the noise?
   R: I'll speak to the manager.
5 Q: Can I help you?
   R: Yes, I hope so. It's about our bags.

Unit 6

1.32

W: What are you looking at? Oh, recipes! Are you going to make something?

M: Yes, I've invited some friends round for supper on Saturday, but I can't decide what to cook.

W: Are they close friends?

M: Well, yes, but why do you ask?

W: Because it will help you to make up your mind. If they're good friends, then it's their company that's important, so maybe it doesn't matter what you cook.

M: That's a good point. But even though they're close friends, I still want to make them a nice meal. So I'm thinking, I could make cheese soufflé … or prawn curry … or just a simple steak?

W: Cheese soufflé's quite difficult, isn't it? Can I make a suggestion?

M: Of course!

W: Make something you can prepare in advance. Then you won't have to spend so much time in the kitchen when they arrive.

M: Another good point! Anyway, all this talk about food is making me hungry! Do you fancy a sandwich?

1.33

Welcome back. You're listening to KLH radio. We heard about the film *Australia* earlier in the programme. Well, I've just come back from a trip to Australia and one of the places I visited was the Kakadu National Park near Darwin up in the north. The park is run by the government and the traditional Aboriginal owners, and it's in a beautiful area. Visitors are only allowed to go into certain parts of the park, and for some trips you have to go with a guide.

Well, I met an Aboriginal woman there who takes tourists into the outback and shows them how to survive on the food you can find there. They call this food bush tucker. Well, standing in the park with the Aboriginal guide, I looked around me and to be honest I couldn't see that there was that much to eat. There were a few trees and a lot of grass – but it was dry, brown grass, and there wasn't much else. Then the Aboriginal woman waded into a watering hole, which I thought was taking a risk because of the crocodiles. There are crocodile warning signs all through the area saying you shouldn't do that. But I later found

out that the Aborigines sometimes eat the younger small crocodiles. And they also collect crocodile eggs.

So, from the watering hole she collected some water lilies. The stalks were like celery, so we chewed on them and that was OK. And they had these little balls attached which we also ate. So far, so good. Then she dug up some grass and we ate part of the roots – they call them bush carrots.

Then she showed us a tree and said it was a good cure for sore throats, colds and headaches. She pulled a handful of leaves off the tree and in the bundle of leaves there was an ants' nest. She took a handful of ants and started to crush them quickly in her hand. I think you have to do this quickly because the ants bite. So we ate them – the crushed ants – too. They had a lemon flavour – it was the best thing we ate that day. Really, we had a complete dinner right there from what had appeared to be nothing at all! I don't think you should do this without a guide, though.

1.34

2 You have to picnic in designated areas.
5 You have to contact the warden in advance of your visit.
6 You don't have to show identification on entry.
8 You have to report any accidents or incidents with wild animals.

1.35

1 If you go to the gym,
2 You'll feel better
3 You won't lose weight
4 I'll tell you about my diet

a when I see you.
b you'll get fit.
c unless you give up junk food.
d if you change your diet.

1.36

In today's show, we hear about two people who decided to try and get away from the 24-hour lifestyle and so-called rat race of modern life. The first by travelling to a different culture, the second by radically changing his way of life without leaving his own culture. What did their experiences teach them? How easy is it – or is it even possible – to break out of the restrictions and expectations of modern society?

So first, radio journalist Lisa Napoli. She was on a search for meaning in her life when someone suggested she head to Bhutan. No 1960s-style hippy traveller, Napoli actually went to Bhutan with a high-profile job – to help in the setting up of a new radio station. She fell in love with the country and recently wrote a book titled *Radio Shangri-La: What I Learned in Bhutan, the Happiest Kingdom on Earth*. In her book, Napoli describes how learning to live with less made her life richer. She explains that in Bhutan it was impossible to live a frenetic 24/7 lifestyle. So many people think they need and enjoy having a lot of stuff, but what if that's not possible? For Napoli, the key is to appreciate what is around you rather than to constantly desire and strive for things you do not have. If we value simplicity and respect the natural environment, we will be more content, she feels.

But how quickly can we adapt to a different culture in this way? Napoli found that for her it was easy. What about attempting to live in a different way within your own culture? There must be so much pressure to conform to what is around you. How determined do you have to be to ignore that? One person who knows is a man called Mark Boyle. He decided to give up using money for a year. How did he manage? He soon discovered if you want to live with no money, you will need a lot more time. Even routine tasks such as washing clothes takes a couple of hours instead of just thirty minutes in a washing machine. He had to cycle everywhere as he had no money to get the bus or train – but on the other hand, he didn't need to pay for expensive gym membership any more. Perhaps the most valuable lesson that Mark Boyle learned was the value of friendship, community and relationships based on trust not money.

So if you *are* fed up with the modern pace of life, how realistic is it to make changes like this? Maybe you don't need to be so radical – there are other ways of slowing down that might be just as effective. You won't know unless you try.

🎵 1.37
1   Are you comfortable at this table?
2   Good evening. Do you have a reservation?
3   They're a national chain.
4   It's hard to eat well when you're travelling.

🎵 1.39
1   Q: Are you ready to order?
    R: Not quite. We just need a minute.
2   Q: Would you like something to drink?
    R: Yes, I'll have a bottle of sparkling water, please.
3   Q: And for your main course?
    R: I'll have the cod.
4   Q: Would you like to see the dessert menu?
    R: No, thanks. We'll just have coffee.
5   Q: Did you enjoy your meal?
    R: Yes, it was all delicious, thanks.

Unit 7

🎵 1.41
1   When I was little, I used to live with my grandparents.
2   Who did you use to live with?
3   I didn't use to like my school.
4   Did you use to enjoy going to school?
5   We didn't use to play outside very often.
6   Where did you use to play?

🎵 1.42
All great cities change over time. Timbuktu, in Mali, is an example of this. Timbuktu used to be a thriving city and an important place of learning for Islam. Centuries ago, it played a huge role in the spread of Islam in Africa. Even today, three important mosques still exist and Timbuktu is the home of one of the world's great collections of ancient manuscripts. The great teachings of Islam, from astronomy and mathematics to medicine and law, were collected and produced here in several hundred thousand manuscripts. This heritage is recognised by the inclusion of Timbuktu on the list of World Heritage Sites.

Timbuktu's geographical location was an important factor in its history. It was at the crossroads of major trading routes. The River Niger passes through Timbuktu on its 4,000-kilometre journey from Guinea in the west to the Niger delta in Nigeria. Camel trains used to pass through the city continuously on their way north and south. They would bring gold from the mining areas in the south and salt from the north. The river also used to bring cargoes of gold, as well as slaves, to the city. People from all of the major North African cities would come here to exchange horses and cloth for gold. Equally, scholars from places as far away as Cairo and Baghdad came to teach and study.

In the 16th century, Timbuktu was invaded by Moroccan forces. The scholars began to leave and the trade routes also started to move closer to the coast. The golden age of the city was over.

🎵 1.43
19.20.21 What is it? A simple sequence of numbers or something more meaningful than that? In fact, it's the name of a fascinating project about modern cities. The man responsible for this project is the architect Richard Saul Wurman. His project is about collecting information on 19 cities that will have more than 20 million people in the 21st century.

How and why did he get the idea for a project like this? What's it all about? In the year 2008, for the first time in history, there were more people living inside cities than outside them. This is one of the biggest changes in the way we live that we have ever seen. Wurman looked on the Internet and tried to find the appropriate books and lists that would give him information – data, maps, and so on – so that he could understand why urban life is getting more and more popular. And as he couldn't find what he was looking for, he decided to collect the data himself. And the 19.20.21 project was born.

So, why do we move to cities? People are pulled towards cities because that's where they have greater opportunities. Cities are where you put museums, where you put universities, where you put the centres of government and business. The inventions, the discoveries, the music and art in our world, all take place in these places where people come together.

The cities that the 19.20.21 project is looking at are those of extremes, the most obvious extreme being size. A thousand years ago, the biggest city was Cordoba in Spain. Three hundred years ago, it was Beijing – a century ago London, then New York City in 1950, and today it's Tokyo. But the fastest growing city today is Lagos in Nigeria. So the interesting cities are the ones that are clearly the largest, the oldest, the fastest growing (like Lagos), the most densely populated (that's Mumbai in India), or the least dense which cover the largest area, like Los Angeles.

If we want to make things better – not worse – in our cities, then we need to understand them. We need to be able to compare them. We have to understand before we act. And although there are a lot of little ideas for making things better – reduce traffic jams, increase safety, have cleaner air – you can't solve the problem with a collection of little ideas. So, the 19.20.21 project brings together the information we need.

🎵 1.44
1   Do you usually get the bus or walk?
2   Do you want to go out or stay in?
3   Do you prefer action films or romances?
4   Do you prefer watching TV or reading?
5   Would you prefer tea or coffee?

🎵 1.45
1   Q: Do you usually get the bus or walk?
    R: I prefer to walk because it's better for me.
2   Q: Do you want to go out or stay in?
    R: I'd rather go out. It's the weekend.
3   Q: Do you prefer action films or romances?
    R: Romances. I find action films a bit boring.
4   Q: Do you prefer watching TV or reading?
    R: I prefer watching TV. It's much more entertaining.
5   Q: Would you prefer tea or coffee?
    R: Tea, please. I've already had several cups of coffee today.

Unit 8

🎵 2.1
Easter Island, or Rapa Nui, is one of the world's most isolated inhabited islands. It's part of the Polynesian islands in the South Pacific Ocean, but it's 2,000 kilometres away from the nearest inhabited island – Pitcairn Island – and 3,000 kilometres from the coast of Chile. Easter Island is

famous for its colossal stone statues. There are more than 800 of these huge human figures, called *moai*, at various sites around the island. The statues are carved out of volcanic stone and they represent the islanders' ancestors.

Carbon-dating suggests that the *moai* were carved over a period of about 600 years, ending about 400 years ago. Some of the *moai* are wearing 'hats' – round red stone additions to the top of the statues. These hats, or *pukao*, are over two metres high. It seems probable that the *pukao* meant high status to the ancient Polynesians, so the figures with *pukao* might have been especially important people. The *pukao* must have been added after the main figure was carved since they are made from a different type of rock. California State University archaeologist Carl Lipo believes the Polynesians rolled the *pukao* along the ground and up ramps eight metres high to the top of the statues. He says the islanders were incredible engineers and managed to move heavy objects using relatively few men.

2.2
1 I must have seen it before, I think.
2 It can't have been on before.
3 I may have seen a trailer.
7 You might have been busy.
9 They could have phoned by mistake.

2.3
1 She must have been in a hurry.
2 He mightn't have realised the time.
3 It might have been on a different channel.
4 They can't have forgotten.
5 He must have switched it off.

2.4
The strange and fascinating phenomenon of crop circles – which actually aren't simply circular but form intricate geometric patterns in farm fields – has inspired many possible explanations over the years. Crop-circle enthusiasts who prefer para-normal explanations for the circles believe that they must be messages left behind by extraterrestrial visitors, while more conventionally scientific-minded people have theorised that they might have resulted from natural physical forces, such as wind or heat. But now, there's another, even more bizarre, explanation: wallabies.

As the BBC News and many other news outlets are reporting, Lara Giddings, Attorney General for the Australian state of Tasmania, told a Parliamentary hearing that wallabies have been eating poppies in fields that provide legal opium for morphine and other painkillers. Apparently, according to Giddings, the wallabies are eating the poppies and then becoming so disoriented that they run around in the fields erratically, creating paths that resemble crop circles.

An official with an Australian poppy-cultivation company told ABC News that in the process of consuming the poppy-seed capsules, the wallabies often also eat some of the substances that cause opium's hallucinogenic effect in humans. The weird suggestion that animals may have been the cause of Australian crop circles, however, doesn't really explain the crop-circle phenomenon. Are they capable of creating the sort of intricate geometric patterns seen in most crop circles? What about the crop circles found thousands of kilometres away from Australia, in the UK?

This odd explanation also doesn't account for the alternative view that crop circles are nothing more than elaborate jokes. A University of Oregon physicist, Richard Taylor, speculates that crop-circle hoaxers may now be using increasingly sophisticated tools such as GPS devices and laser pointers to burn complex patterns into fields.

2.6
1 S: Look! It's snowing outside.
   R: Are you sure?
2 S: I'm getting married.
   R: You're having me on!
3 S: Someone in Siberia has seen a yeti.
   R: Come off it!
4 S: I read in the paper that there are no fish left in the sea.
   R: You must be joking!
5 S: The date on today's newspaper is 2025.
   R: They must have made a mistake.
6 S: From next year, the clocks change to ten-hour days.
   R: That can't be right!

2.7
1 Environmentalists in Taiwan have been helping frogs to cross a road and get to a river safely for the last three years. During the month of October, a wildlife group in the north of the country monitors the road with the help of local students. The aim is to avoid frog deaths. Campaigners say that frogs are increasingly under threat as humans move into their habitat.
2 In Holland this month, an unusual new ice cream is going on sale. The main ingredient is camel's milk. The producers have used camel's milk because it has less fat and more vitamins than normal milk.

Unit 9

2.9
A: Have you had any ideas about a present for Aunt Jane yet?
B: Well, I know we want to buy something really special and unusual, but I haven't really had any good ideas so far.
A: Why don't we look on the Internet? Type in *luxury gifts* or something like that and see what comes up.
B: OK … Let's see.
A: There, look – gold. You can't get more special than gold.
B: Do you think she'd like jewellery? She doesn't seem to wear it much – just earrings and a plain gold chain.
A: Well, maybe if we got something custom-made. It says here that items can be made to the customer's specification from a selection of designs.
B: Yeah, that's worth thinking about. What else is there?
A: Oh, click on that rug! I've always loved these hand-made rugs. What does it say about them?
B: 'Our traditional hand-woven rugs are still being made today using the same techniques and quality materials as hundreds of years ago … these classic designs have not been altered for centuries … and are imported direct from the producer… .' OK, that's another possibility, but I'm sure I read somewhere about some carpets that are made by children working in terrible conditions.
A: Yes, but can you see that logo? It's the GoodWeave logo. It means that the carpet factories have been inspected, so the ones on this website are OK.
B: So, let's just check the prices, though. It sounds like they might cost a fortune. Wow!
A: Yeah … OK, let's try something else … what's this?
B: Oh yeah, silk. Well, that used to be a luxury thing, but is it still so special?
A: What about old silk? That's different. Here's a section on antique silk wall hangings. They're gorgeous.
B: Yeah, that's a good idea, I suppose. If they aren't made any more, it's unique.
A: OK, so most of these antique textiles were made in Vietnam and Laos, and can't be found anywhere else. It says they've been carefully selected and they only sell pieces that are in excellent condition, despite their age.
A: Well, what do you think? Is there something here we could buy her?

2.10
1 This one was hand-made,
2 but these days they are mass-produced.
3 It's been used to put flowers in for the last ten years.
4 It's made of thick blue glass
5 and it contained some kind of medicine originally.

2.11
For those of you who enjoy long train journeys, we have news of a new route which will soon be completed. Eventually, you'll able to go by rail all the way from London to the Caspian Sea. Much of this epic railway has already been built across the Caucasus Mountains. The Baku–Tbilisi–Kars railway – or BTK railway – will link the Azerbaijani capital of Baku with Kars, in Turkey. Then a rail tunnel underneath Istanbul will be opened in the next few years, linking East and West in an echo of the trade routes of 1,000 years ago. Both passengers and goods will be carried, and the rail link will transport oil products west and take European goods east.

One of the first east–west trade routes was, of course, the Silk Road, which was made famous to many by the Italian merchant Marco Polo about 700 years ago. Marco Polo's journal tells us many details of the trade that was carried out between China, India, Arabia and Europe. Luxurious silks, aromatic spices and precious stones were imported from the East, and cargoes of fine glassware and exotic perfumes were exported from Europe. While goods such as paper, ink and silk were transported west across the overland routes – the Silk Road – there were other products, such as Chinese ceramics, that had to be transported by sea. These sea-trade routes had been used since long before the time of Marco Polo, and in the centuries after Marco Polo's time they became much more important. Spices in particular – such as black pepper, cinnamon, cardamom and ginger – were brought from Asia to Europe and the control of these sea-trade routes was the driving force behind the European exploration which is known as 'the Age of Discovery'. The Portuguese, Spanish and British Empires were all based on keeping control of both the routes and the places where spices and other goods were produced. Nowadays, of course, it's oil rather than spices which drives the world economy. And there is no doubt that oil from the Caspian Sea is the main reason why the new rail link across the Caucasus Mountains is being built.

2.13
A = assistant, C = customer
1 A: Can I help you at all?
   C: No, thanks. I'm just looking.
2 A: Is it for you?
   C: No, it's for my mother.
3 A: Would you like me to gift-wrap it?
   C: No thanks, that's OK.
4 A: Do you want to pay by card or in cash?
   C: I'll use my card.
5 A: What time is best for us to deliver it?
   C: Morning, any day of the week.

Unit 10

2.15
W: How was your trip to Canada?
M: It was absolutely stunning, but I wouldn't like to live there.
W: Really? Why is that?
M: I think it would be difficult for me to get used to the cold weather. It was 15 degrees below zero some days! The local people don't seem to notice it so much.
W: If I lived somewhere that cold, I'd never leave the house! Even if I had the warmest, high-tech clothes!

M: Well, they have lots of stuff that makes life a bit easier. For example, you can start your car without leaving the house, and this warms up the engine and heats up the inside of the car before you get in.
W: Really? That's a good idea. How does that work?
M: It's just like a remote-control thing – you know, like locking and unlocking the car from a distance.
W: Oh yeah. Well, that would be good if you had to go out when it was really cold. I reckon I would eat a lot in a climate like that, though. I'd put on loads of weight, sitting at home, eating, looking at the snow through the window!
M: You say that, but I'm sure it would be different if you really lived there.
W: Maybe. I'd rather live somewhere hot, though. It's easier to stay cool than to get warm.
M: Do you think so? If you had air conditioning in your house, do you mean?
W: Yes, sort of. But also you could avoid the heat quite easily, I reckon. Get up early when it's cool, have a siesta in the middle of the day, that kind of thing.
M: I don't like sleeping in the afternoon very much.
W: OK, but you would have to rest – even if you didn't sleep – if it was over 40 degrees outside.
M: I just couldn't imagine living like that.
W: So really what you're saying is, you're happy where you are?
M: Yes, I suppose so. Aren't I lucky?

2.16
1 I'm not sure you would feel that way
2 If I lived somewhere that cold,
3 Well, it would make it warmer
4 You could deal with the hot afternoons

a I'd never go outside.
b if you had a good fire.
c if you had a siesta.
d if you really lived there.

2.17
P = presenter, G = guest
P: It's time once again for our 'CineScience' feature, where we look at how films deal with science and how realistically they show scientific ideas. This week our guest is the neurologist, Dr Clare Law. We're looking at the film *Limitless*, which has been in cinemas recently and is now out on DVD. The idea of the film is that we only use 20 per cent of our brain power. What would happen if we could use all 100 per cent of our brain's potential? Well, in the film, the main character takes a special pill that lets him do exactly that. And what happens? He writes a book. He learns to speak Italian. He becomes a master of martial arts. So, Clare, does that mean that we could all be like this if we knew how to take advantage of our brains properly?
G: Well, sadly, it's just a film. And as is often the case in films, the science is not 100 per cent accurate. Of course, it would be unrealistic to think there was a special pill that could unlock our brain power in a flash. But it's not even true that we only use 20 per cent of our brain. It's not as simple as that. What actually happens is that we use different parts of the brain at different times and for different functions. So, if you were walking to work, the part of your brain that deals with physical movement would be active. If you were making a cake, then a different part of your brain would be busy. In other words, there are no unused or hidden regions that are waiting to be discovered and exploited. It would be incredibly inefficient for our bodies to only use 20 per cent of the brain. We're using all of our brain all day and we actually already have limitless brain power.

P: So, that's good news. And remember what the character in the film did with his limitless power. Wrote a book, learned a language and a new skill. It doesn't take a genius to achieve this. These are things which we could all manage to do – if we used our own limitless brain power more efficiently.

G: Exactly.

2.19

1 S: I think I was bitten by a mosquito during the night.
  R: Why don't you put some of this cream on?
2 S: Look at my finger! I've cut it on something. It's bleeding.
  R: You'd better wash it under the tap.
3 S: My ankle is really painful and I can't walk.
  R: If I were you, I'd go to A&E and get it X-rayed.
4 S: My son has been feeling sick since he ate those oysters.
  R: He might be allergic to them – I'd keep an eye on him.
5 S: I did something to my wrist last week and it still hurts.
  R: Really? You're best getting it looked at.

Unit 11

2.20

I = interviewer, G = guest

I: It's often said that good news never makes the headlines. And it's true that we don't usually hear about wildlife issues unless there's a disaster or a catastrophe somewhere. Then for a day or maybe two, we see front-page headlines and lurid images on our television screens. But there are many success stories. The challenge has always been to tell the rest of the world what's going on. Jo Makeba is going to tell us more.

G: Yes, well, you might imagine that in these days of the Internet, we don't have to rely so much on traditional media like the press to get our message to a wide audience. And you'd be right. Today we can publish our own photos, videos and stories directly onto the Internet for everyone to see.

I: And so how does that affect people working in wildlife?

G: Well, basically it means that small-scale organisations can have a direct connection with the public.

I: The people who might be interested in their work?

G: Yes, and also of course, the people who might be able to fund their work. I'm sure we've all heard of the legendary conservationist, Richard Leakey. Well, he saw that the Internet was a way of connecting individual members of the public with the people who were working on the frontlines of wildlife conservation. Richard set up WildlifeDirect. The current director of WildlifeDirect is Paula Kahumbu, who actually lived close to Richard Leakey when she was growing up.

I: And what exactly is WildlifeDirect?

G: It's an online platform which gives about 120 projects a way of sharing their day-to-day challenges and victories via blogs, diaries, videos, photos and podcasts. So you don't need to wait for a story to make it into the news. Through the WildlifeDirect website, you can spend your lunch break following Maasai warriors, protecting lions in Africa, seeing how conservationists are saving orphan orang-utans in Indonesia, or watching an endangered eagle after an eye operation.

I: An eagle that had had an eye operation?

G: Well, this is a great example of the power of direct communication. Paula explained to me that Rosy, an eagle in Kenya, had been with his mate for 25 years, raising new eagle chicks every year. When he grew blind and stopped mating, the website published his story. People then donated enough money to perform cataract surgery which successfully replaced his lenses, and now he is practically back to a normal life.

I: And can I see him on the WildlifeDirect site?
G: Yes, exactly.

2.21

1 You said you knew how to do that.
2 They said it was in the paper.
3 They asked me if I would feed their cat.
4 You said you weren't hungry.
5 You said you could speak Russian.
6 You said you'd tidied up.

2.23

How does language change over time? Are there words that we simply stop using? Are there words that we have been using for hundreds or even thousands of years? And how will languages change in this age of global media and social networking? Researchers at the University of Reading, in the United Kingdom, have been investigating exactly these questions.

Biologist Mark Pagel has studied 87 languages from Europe, the Middle East and the Indian subcontinent which are all related to each other. He took 200 words which he knew had a shared history going back 9,000 years. Words like *who* and *three*, and their equivalents in the 87 different languages. The list of 200 words includes nouns like *salt* and *name*, verbs like *give* and *stand*, and adjectives like *new* and *yellow*. With the help of a computer program, Pagel analysed all the data relating to these 200 words. The result of the analysis shows that the five oldest words of the 200 – in other words, the ones that have not changed very much since ancient times – are *I, two, five, three* and *who*. These words have hardly changed their sounds and forms. They are also some of the words that we use most in day-to-day speech and so that could be the reason why they have been so stable. The computer analysis, as well as taking a lot less time to look at the data, also highlights patterns that might be difficult to see. For example, it reveals that in all the languages in the study, verbs and adjectives change faster than nouns. Now it's the job of the human analysts to come up with an explanation for this.

2.24

1 Can I call you back?
2 Could you ring me later?
3 Could you leave your name?
4 Can you give me your number?
5 Can you tell him I called?
6 Could you ask her to phone me?

2.25

P = patient, R = receptionist

1 P: Can I speak to the doctor, please?
  R: I'm afraid the doctor is with a patient at the moment.
2 P: Oh dear, it's about my next appointment.
  R: OK, could you give me your name?
3 P: Yes, it's John Watson. I can't get to my appointment today.
  R: OK, thanks. Can I give you a new appointment time?
4 P: Thanks. Can you make it in the morning, please?
  R: Of course. Can you come on Friday at nine o'clock?
5 P: Yes, that's fine. Thanks.
  R: Thank you for calling. Bye.

Unit 12

2.27

1

W: Nice to see you back. Are you feeling better now?
M: Yes, a lot better actually since I finished that course of tablets.
W: What were they? Antibiotics?

M: Yes. I can't imagine what we would do without antibiotics. And apparently it was just by chance that they were discovered.

W: I know. But I think that even if Fleming hadn't discovered them – or penicillin, anyway – some other scientist would have done eventually.

M: Yes, I suppose so. There was so much medical research going on in those days.

W: And today, as well.

2

A: I wonder if all those actors would have become so famous if they hadn't made any Harry Potter films.

B: You mean the ones who play the kids in the films? I suppose so. They would have been in other films.

A: Of course, there wouldn't have been any Harry Potter films if JK Rowling hadn't written the books first. Have you read them?

B: No, have you?

A: Just the first one. I probably would have read more if I'd been a bit younger when they came out.

B: My dad's read a couple!

A: Really?

3

D= Dad, P = Paul

D: I can't find that website you told me about, Paul.

P: Have you typed it in correctly? Let's see. Look, you've left a bit out.

D: What?

P: The forward slashes after 'http'. Actually, I read that Tim Berners-Lee said he could have left them out.

D: Well, it would have been a lot easier if he had! I wouldn't have wasted so much time typing.

P: Actually Dad, it's easier if you copy and paste the address in.

D: Well, I could have done that if the address had been on the screen somewhere! But you told me it on the phone.

P: Or you could have used Google …

D: Oh yes. I suppose so. I hadn't thought of Google.

4

A: Did you see the film they made about Dian Fossey?

B: Yes, I thought it was pretty good. It makes you wonder what might have happened if she'd lived.

A: But why was she murdered, really?

B: It's never been properly investigated. She might have upset the local poachers too many times.

A: But she'd always had problems with them – or at least that's what it said in the film.

B: Exactly. Or it might have been because she'd had a lot of trouble with the authorities. She was against that kind of wildlife tourism that goes into remote areas.

A: Well, one thing's for sure, the gorillas would be better protected if she was still alive.

2.28

1 Captain Scott led two expeditions to Antarctica.
2 On the second, they were racing another team to the South Pole.
3 This picture shows team members preparing a sledge.
4 Some people say they might have been the first to the South Pole
5 if they hadn't used this type of transport.
6 And they might not have died on the return journey.

2.29

I suppose that in one way, we could say that all animals have to be experts at what they do. If they weren't, well, they wouldn't survive. The truth is that the day-to-day life of most animals is about finding something to eat while trying not to become food for another animal. So we could say that, for example, the polar bear or the lion is an expert hunter. Or the chameleon is an expert at camouflage. But some animals seem to us to be particularly skilled. These are the ones that seem to be able to take their expertise to a different level, especially in a laboratory or a controlled study environment.

Let's take the octopus as an example. These marine animals can do extraordinary things in their natural habitat. The common octopus can almost instantaneously mimic the colours, patterns and even textures of its surroundings. Predators swim by without even noticing it. And if a predator does notice it, the octopus squirts a cloud of black ink at the predator, which gives it just enough time to get quickly away.

But we can see how clever the octopus really is when we take it out of its natural environment and bring it into the laboratory. Put a nice tasty food item like a prawn in a closed jar, and then put the jar in a tank. Next, put an octopus in the tank as well. It will actually take the lid off the jar to get at the prawn! So not only does the octopus work out how to get into the jar, it also has the physical ability to do it. And that's not all. At a laboratory in Seattle, in the United States, a giant Pacific octopus was actually getting out of its tank at night, going to the other tanks and eating the fish in them, then going back to its own tank. It was only the trail of water on the floor that gave the laboratory staff a clue to what was going on!

2.31

1 S: You forgot to text me!
   R: Oh yes. Sorry about that!
2 S: I'm so sorry. I didn't have time to cook anything special.
   R: There's no need to apologise. It's not a problem.
3 S: This door is open!
   R: It's my fault. I forgot to lock it.
4 S: I'm sorry, but I think I've lost the magazine you lent me.
   R: Don't worry about it. I'd already read it.
5 S: I can't believe I forgot about that! I'm really sorry.
   R: It's not your fault. It could have happened to anyone.

2.32 IELTs practice test

Presenter: In this test you'll hear a number of different recordings and you'll have to answer questions on what you hear. There will be time for you to read the instructions and questions, and you will have a chance to check your answers. In the IELTs listening test, the recording will be played once only. The test is in four sections.

Now turn to section one on page 100 of your book. You will hear a student called Joanna telling her friend about an arts festival which is being held in the city where they are studying. First you have some time to look at questions 1 and 2. You will see that there is also an example which has been done for you.

Presenter: Now we shall begin. You should answer the questions as you listen because you will not hear the recording a second time. Listen carefully and answer questions 1 and 2.

Dave: Hi, Joanna. Where have you been?

Joanna: Hi, Dave. I had to go into college to return a DVD I'd borrowed from the library.

Dave: Oh right.

Joanna: But while I was there, I got some information about the City Arts festival that starts next week.

Dave:	Oh yeah. I saw a poster advertising it somewhere.
Joanna:	Yeah, and I picked up this leaflet from the library. It gives you the website address, so as I was there, I logged on to get more information. Actually, although they've got the full programme of events fixed now, you can't book online, which seems strange. There's a number to phone, though.
Dave:	And are there student discounts?
Joanna:	I guess so, but I didn't notice. Anyway, there are three things I'd like to see: an Italian film, a rock concert and an art exhibition. The exhibition's free and you don't need to book, so I'll definitely go to that. But I'm going to get tickets for the film, in case they sell out.
Dave:	Good idea. You can always buy concert tickets at the door, because that's in a really big hall.
Joanna:	Right.
Presenter:	Before you listen to the rest of the conversation, you have some time to read questions 3 to 10.
Presenter:	Now listen and answer questions 3 to 10.
Dave:	So when does the festival actually start?
Joanna:	Well, it's usually held the first week of October, but it's earlier this year for some reason. The opening night is September 20th and events go on till the end of the month.
Dave:	And have you got that phone number?
Joanna:	Yeah, it's here ... look ... it's 0967 990776.
Dave:	OK. I'll write it down. 0967 990776, thanks.
Joanna:	I thought the local council made a profit from the festival, but it says here that there's a commercial sponsor – it's a local bank. I didn't know that.
Dave:	Neither did I. What other events have they got on?
Joanna:	Umm. As well as the art exhibitions and stuff that's open every day, there are special events each day. Like on Monday there's a musical in the City Hall. That's only £3.65 for students.
Dave:	I think I'll give that a miss – I've got football training on Mondays. But I'm free on Wednesday.
Joanna:	There's a jazz band on then, and that's only £2.50 for students.
Dave:	Sounds good. Is that in the City Hall too? We could go.
Joanna:	Well, I'm busy actually – but it's at the sports centre if you're interested.
Dave:	Oh right.
Joanna:	Thursday's the cheapest event – only £1.25 for students – and it's on in the library. Can you guess what it is?
Dave:	Probably the college choir.
Joanna:	Actually no – they've not been asked apparently. No, it's a poetry evening.
Dave:	Umm. Isn't there any modern dance on anywhere?
Joanna:	On Friday. That's at the college. It's quite expensive though, £15.00 for adults and £12.75 for students.
Dave:	Yes, that is a lot. If I'm going to spend that much, I'd prefer to go out on Saturday.
Joanna:	Yes, me too. But on Saturday night there isn't live music or a party or anything – just the fireworks in the city park – and that's only £1.50.
Dave:	Yeah that'd be good.
Presenter:	Now turn to Section 2 on page 101 of your book. You will hear some information about a medical museum in London called the Hunterian Museum, which is part of the Royal College of Surgeons. First you have some time to look at questions 11 to 15.

Presenter:	Now listen and answer questions 11 to 15.
Woman:	Good evening. I'm here to tell you about the Hunterian Museum in London, which is part of the Royal College of Surgeons. Although a medical museum, it is open to the general public. The museum specialises in the history of the study of anatomy, and especially the work of John Hunter in the eighteenth century.

If you would like a free guided tour of the museum, then come along at one o'clock any Wednesday. Spaces on the tour are limited to twenty-five though, so it's best to reserve a place by phone, and these tours are for individual members of the public, families and small groups of friends only.

Tours for groups of school students can also be arranged and these are also free of charge. Teachers are encouraged to make a donation of around £3.00 per student if they can afford it, but this isn't obligatory. What teachers must do, however, is phone to agree a time in advance as only one school party's allowed in at a time. Then there's an online booking form which you can use to confirm the booking, or just send a letter if you prefer.

For older students and adult groups, we provide more specialised tours, and these cost £100 for a short tour of thirty minutes, or if you want a slightly longer one, it's £130 for forty-five minutes. There is a student discount, however, so college groups would pay £75 for the shorter tour, for example.

In terms of facilities available at the museum, teachers and others should bear in mind that space is very limited. As we're in the centre of London with many cafés and restaurants nearby, refreshments aren't sold on site, though there is a small shop selling souvenirs. Most of the things on show in the museum are preserved animal specimens in glass cases, so there are no interactive displays aimed at small children. And our tours are only in English, although there is printed material available in other major languages on request. There's also a lecture room which groups can book for an extra charge, and this is equipped with power-point projector and microscopes.

Presenter:	Before you hear the rest of the presentation, you have some time to look at questions 16 to 20.
Presenter:	Now listen and answer questions 16 to 20.
Woman:	Next, a bit about the history of the museum, and the preserved animal and plant specimens you can see there. The museum's named after John Hunter, who was a pioneer in the study of anatomy. He was among the first to understand that the study of other animals could tell us a lot about how the human body works.

John Hunter was born in 1728 and came to London to work as an assistant in an anatomy school in 1748. Here John did his training in the study of human anatomy. It was after 1760, however, that he turned his attention to animals. That's when he became a surgeon in the army, spending three years in France and Portugal, where he started collecting and preserving animal specimens, such as lizards.

On his return to London in 1763, Hunter set up in private practice and started to build up his collection of specimens. When he moved to a big house in Leicester Square in 1783, Hunter started to take in resident students and gave the name 'teaching museum' to his collection. By the time of his death in 1793, Hunter had collected specimens from all over the world, including the first kangaroo to be seen outside Australia. He had 14,000 different exhibits, with 500 species of plants and animals represented. And many of these specimens can still be seen in the museum today, because in 1799 the collection was purchased by the government, who presented it to the Royal College of Surgeons. And they've been looking after it ever since, which is why the Hunterian Museum is located in their building in London to this day.

Presenter: Now turn to Section 3 on page 102 of your book. You will hear a student called Sarah talking to her college tutor about some research she has to do as part of her course. First you have some time to look at questions 21 to 27.

Presenter: Now listen and answer questions 21 to 27.
Man: Hello, Sarah.
Sarah: Hi.
Man: So you want to talk about your research project?
Sarah: That's right. I want to find out how many people use the tourist information office and what they think of the service they get.
Man: Interesting. Have you written your proposal yet?
Sarah: No, that's what I wanted to ask you about. What should I include? Someone said I should make a list of my aims first.
Man: Well, I don't know about a list. A statement of aims is the correct term. It's just a quick summary of what you hope to get out of the project.
Sarah: OK. And should I include other documents I've prepared? Like the questionnaire? I'm still working on that.
Man: I can check that later. But I think it's good to prepare an information sheet for participants – it would help you to think about interview methods. It'd be good to see that soon.
Sarah: Oh right. And I want the project to have statistical data, not just to be a collection of opinions.
Man: That's good. So that should be clear from the proposal too.
Sarah: Great. So what else must I include in the proposal? Or are some things optional?
Man: OK. Some things that people normally put in a research proposal don't really apply to you. Like any costs involved – that can be really important in some research projects. But as we don't have a budget, it's not something you need to include. Any costs have to come out of your own pocket, I'm afraid.
Sarah: Yes, I understand that.
Man: But I do need to know your criteria for choosing who to interview – I've got to check that you're using good sampling principles, for example.
Sarah: Sure. And what about the way I'm going to analyse my findings?
Man: That's not essential at the proposal stage on this project, but if you've got some ideas, include them because it could save time later.
Sarah: OK. And do I need to make it clear how the report will be organised?
Man: Oh, I'm going to be giving you a template to use, so there's no need to go into that in the proposal.

Sarah: Great. Thanks.
Presenter: Before you hear the rest of the conversation, you have some time to look at questions 28 to 30.

Presenter: Now listen and answer questions 28 to 30.
Man: Actually, another thing we could discuss now is making sound recordings of interviews.
Sarah: Oh right. Do I have to record them all? I could try to get as many as possible, but it'd be rather expensive.
Man: Yes, don't worry. You only need a few, chosen randomly, just to give an idea of how the interviews are going. You can send one in each time you update me on your progress.
Sarah: OK. How often should I do that? I haven't done a timetable for the interviews yet, but they'll be spread over three or four weeks – with about 200 in total. I reckon on doing twenty a day.
Man: Umm. Let me know how you're getting on at the end of each day's interviewing then, whether you've had any problems or not. It can be a lonely job.
Sarah: Thanks. I appreciate that.
Man: And what about the confidentiality of participants? Because that can cause problems.
Sarah: Well, I'm getting them to sign a consent form. It says that I'll only use the information for my research – that I won't pass it on to anyone else. But that's the only promise I'm making. They have to give me their names and agree to their data being stored on the college computer network.
Man: That sounds good. You won't put names in your report, I know, and the data will all get deleted at the end of the year – but we don't promise any of that.
Sarah: Sure.
Presenter: Now turn to Section 4 on page 103 of your book. You will hear part of a lecture about the wildlife on Christmas Island in the Pacific Ocean. First you have some time to look at questions 31 to 35.

Presenter: Now listen and answer questions 31 to 35.
Man: Good evening. Tonight I'm talking about Christmas Island in the Pacific Ocean and its incredible wildlife. First of all, let me explain that Christmas Island is a remote tropical island about 2,600 kilometres northwest of Australia, covering an area of 135 square kilometres, with 73 kilometres of coastline. Around 85 square kilometres has now been made into a national park by the Australian Government, in recognition of the island's unique and threatened wildlife.

Although there's great potential for tourism on the island, the most significant economic activity is currently mining, as there's a good supply of phosphates in the local rock. The role of the national park is therefore to protect the wildlife rather than to attract visitors. Like other remote islands, Christmas Island has a number of unique and endangered species, some of which are already extinct or under threat of extinction. Two rodent species are known to have died out, as has one species of bat, and a number of reptile and bird species are seriously threatened.

The best-known of all the island's creatures, however, are its land crabs which are found in large numbers and which are essential to the island's ecology. And for an 18-day period each year, one of the island's 14 crab species, the red crab, becomes the centre of widespread attention as it makes its spectacular migration to the sea to breed. More about that in a moment.

Aware of the need to do more to protect the fragile eco-system on Christmas Island, the Australian Government has commissioned a report from the Expert Working Group it has set up to investigate the problem. Previous enquiries by government-appointed committees did lead to the setting up of the national park, so there is much to hope for.

Presenter: Before you hear the rest of the lecture, you have some time to look at questions 36 to 40.

Presenter: Now listen and answer questions 36 to 40.
Man: So back to the red crab, which has attracted quite a bit of media attention in recent years. The red crab is found all over Christmas Island and is vital to its eco-system. Although they do sometimes eat snails and other smaller creatures, the crabs' diet is largely made up of leaves, with the addition of flowers and seedlings when these are available. Their droppings then provide an important fertiliser for the island's soil. Also, by turning over the soil when digging the holes called burrows, where they live, the crabs help the propagation of plant species.

Although you might think that an animal that goes in for mass migration would be quite sociable by nature, each red crab actually spends most of the year living alone in its burrow, and so is actually quite solitary. Each crab constructs a burrow in the earth with one chamber inside and one tunnel entrance, and stays there most of the time, especially during the dry season. The crabs are more active in the rainy season and that's also when the famous migration occurs.

It isn't the rain that triggers the migration, however, so much as the phase of the moon and the state of the tides. Trying to predict when the migration will occur is quite difficult, as it can be as early as October or as late as December depending on the year, although it's usually sometime in November in fact.

And when it comes, the migration is quite spectacular with literally millions of crabs heading for the seashore at the same time. Conservationists do their best to limit the number of road casualties among the crabs by closing certain roads, encouraging car sharing and other measures to reduce traffic, even constructing bridges for the crabs at certain key points.

So before I go on to ....

Presenter: That is the end of the test.

Answer key

Unit 1

1a (pages 4 and 5)

1
purple

2
1 F   2 F   3 T   4 T   5 F

3
1 spend   2 seems … like   3 belong   4 possess
5 feel   6 need   7 are disappearing   8 move   9 is getting
10 are speculating

4
1 natural   2 common   3 minority   4 the cold   5 smaller

5
1 use   2 contain   3 come   4 are now reporting
5 is increasing   6 know   7 cause   8 don't understand
9 is becoming

6
1 Do (you) like … Does (it) look   2 'm/am looking
3 does (this bag) belong   4 does (it) taste
5 Are (you) thinking   6 suppose

7
1 He goes out with friends at weekends. *or* At weekends, he goes out with friends.
2 He's / He is spending time with his family today. *or* Today he's / he is spending time with his family.
3 He's / He is making lunch at the moment. *or* At the moment, he's / he is making lunch.
4 He usually makes lunch.
5 He does housework every day. *or* Every day he does housework.
6 He never does DIY.

1b (pages 6 and 7)

1
1 No.
2 Two or more of their senses get mixed up.
3 Yes. It's a bit too much sometimes.
4 Mark's synesthesia means that he tastes words. Kandinsky's synesthesia mixed colour, hearing, touch and smell.
5 Seeing words in colour.
6 Our brains.

2
1 taste   2 hears   3 hearing   4 touch   5 smell

3
1 Where does Mark come from?
  Canada.
2 Who else in his family has the same condition?
  His sister.
3 What's / What is the name of his condition?
  Synesthesia.
4 Which sense gives Mark problems?
  Taste.
5 What is Stevie Wonder famous for?
  He's a musician.
6 What colour does Mark's sister associate with Tuesday?
  Brown.

5b
Possible answers:
1 How many brothers have you got?
2 Do you like your job?

3 Why do you always go to France?
4 Where are you from?
5 Can you speak any other languages?
6 What are your favourite stories?

6
1 luck   2 knowledge   3 power   4 mourning   5 passion

7
1 happiness   2 courage   3 love   4 wisdom   5 sadness

1c (page 8)

1
5

2
1 green   2 men   3 three   4 lead

3
1 ten per cent
2 She can't tell if the DVD player is on or off – because the buttons are red and green.
3 blue
4 red, green, blue
5 police officer, airline pilot

4
1 e   2 g   3 c   4 a   5 d   6 b   7 h   8 f

5
1 A: Louisa is seeing someone new.
2 B: I see. Well, thanks anyway.
3 B: You need to see a doctor.
4 A: Do you see how easy it is?

1d (page 9)

1
1 O: It's a pleasure to meet you.
2 C: Why don't I give you my card?
3 O: May I introduce myself?
4 C: Let's stay in touch.
5 C: It's been good talking to you.
6 O: I'm very pleased to meet you.

2
1 May I introduce myself?
2 It's a pleasure to meet you *or* I'm very pleased to meet you
3 it's been good talking to you. *or* let's stay in touch.
4 Why don't I give you my card?

3
1 for   2 on   3 at   4 in   5 for   6 at

4a
1 e   2 d   3 b   4 c   5 f   6 a

4b
1 2 4 6

5
1 Are you?   2 Is it?   3 Yes, I have.   4 Yes, I do.
5 No, I can't.   6 Are they?

1e (page 10)

1a
1 letter   2 informal   3 known   4 to give information

1b
1 About our work: b c
2 Satisfied customers: a
3 About us: d

2

1 I am working on a new product this year. *or* This year
   I am working on a new product.
2 I can also help you with new projects. *or* Also, I can help
   you with new projects.
3 We are currently advising a national company. *or*
   Currently, we are advising a national company.
4 We are completing a major contract at this time. *or* At this
   time, we are completing a major contract.
5 In addition to this, we have offices in all main cities.
6 We work in TV too.

3

1 designer   2 consultant   3 special   4 dyes
5 developing   6 allergic   7 passion   8 colourful
9 continually   10 painter

Wordbuilding / Learning skills / Check! (page 11)

1

-ist: artist, biologist, scientist
-er/-or: administrator, competitor
-ant: assistant, consultant, participant
-ian: electrician, librarian, musician, politician

2

-er

3

1 librarian   2 artists   3 participants   4 optician
5 photographer   6 electrician

8

1 Japan   2 Brunei   3 France   4 Chicago
5 Mexico   6 Peru
PAPUA NEW GUINEA

Unit 2

2a (pages 12 and 13)

1

1 Kristen   2 Alvaro   3 Theo   4 Carmen   5 Tara

2

1 T   2 N   3 T   4 T

3

1 acrobat   2 juggler   3 living statue   4 puppeteer

4

eight verbs: I've known, I haven't lived, I've felt, I've
never seen, I've just arrived, I've already heard, I've never
experienced, We've been

5

1 We've / We have been here for … we've / we have seen
2 I've / I have performed every night since
3 We've / We have never had
4 My friend has lived here for … I've / I have decided
5 I've / I have always wanted … Since … I've /
   I have become
6 I haven't heard

6

1 Have you seen *Billy Elliot* yet?
2 Don't reserve me a ticket. I've already bought mine.
3 I can't meet you later. I haven't finished my work yet.
4 We've just been to see Lady Gaga. Wow!
5 I arrived this morning and I've already seen dozens
   of performances.
6 I'm not sure what that means! I've just started
   learning Spanish.

8

1 cheerful/melodic   2 unusual   3 lively/rhythmic
4 catchy   5 melancholy/moving   6 tuneless   7 repetitive

2b (pages 14 and 15)

1

1 I really enjoy   2 I hope   3 I keep   4 I need
5 My schedule   6 We decided   7 I finished   8 I agreed

2

a going … to come
b to do
1 b to take   2 a to get   3 b to go   4 b changing
5 a watching   6 b planning   7 b not to give   8 a to do
9 a Seeing

3

1 dancing   2 to introduce   3 to change   4 learning
5 to find   6 joining

4

1 T   2 F   3 F   4 T   5 T

5

1 to do   2 standing   3 to fall   4 going   5 to do
6 Planning   7 dancing

6

1 cry   2 Smile   3 Cheer up   4 laugh … cry
5 laughing … sad   6 smile … smile

7a

1 play   2 tell   3 give   4 sing   5 make   6 write   7 star

7b

1 Authors write plays.
2 Comedians tell jokes.
3 Musicians play instruments.
4 Ordinary people sing karaoke.
5 Politicians give speeches.
6 Rock bands make albums.

2c (page 16)

1

1 because it's about people's lives on one day,
   24 July 2010
2 a documentary
3 ordinary people from 40 different countries
4 no
5 film director Kevin Macdonald's
6 on YouTube

2

1 24 July 2010   2 90 minutes   3 400   4 40   5 4,500
6 81,000   7 192

3

c

4

1 c   2 d   3 b   4 c   5 d   6 e   7 e   8 a   9 a

5

1 had   2 's/has   3 Have … got   4 have   5 've/have
6 have   7 having   8 had

2d (page 17)

1

1 Do you want to, Would you like to
2 Do you feel like, Do you fancy

2

Possible answers:
Yeah, why not?
I like the sound of that.
I'm not keen on him.

3

1 What's on?   2 Who's it by?   3 Who's in it?
4 When / What time is it on?   5 What's it about?

4
1 It was absolutely hilarious.
2 It was absolutely / really awful.
3 It was really / very boring.
4 It was really / very good.
5 It was really / very disappointing.
6 It was absolutely / really brilliant.

6
1 bored   2 amazing   3 disappointed   4 moved
5 depressing   6 fascinating

2e (page 18)

1a
1 therefore   2 both options are correct
3 both options are correct   4 For that reason,   5 so

1b
a Despite being from a classical Indian background, he's had mainstream success in the West.
b He played on Beatles records. Because of this, he quickly became well-known in Europe.
c Although he enjoyed the music he made with the Beatles, he didn't like the attention it brought.
d While he loves Matisse and Picasso, he doesn't believe in owning art.
e He began as a dancer, but he became more interested in making music.
f Although I don't know much about classical Indian music, I love his work.

2
The missing sentences are: 2 a, 3 b, 5 f.
Ravi Shankar is a classical Indian musician who has had huge success over many decades. I've followed his work since I saw him on TV a few years ago. Despite being from a classical Indian background, he's had mainstream success in the West. This began decades ago when he worked with George Harrison, of the Beatles. He played on Beatles records. Because of this he quickly became well-known in Europe. Of course, I'm too young to remember the Beatles. I enjoy the music he makes nowadays. Although I don't know much about classical Indian music, I love his work. I like it because it sounds beautiful and unusual to me. It's really different from Western music. There's so much different stuff out there to listen to, and I enjoy it all.

Wordbuilding / Learning skills / Check! (page 19)

1
bad: actor, influence, mood, student
big: influence, role, statue, success
English: actor, couple, people, student
famous: actor, comedies, couple, people, statue
living: actor, couple, people
mainstream: actor, comedies, success
ordinary: couple, people, role, student
romantic: actor, comedies, couple, mood, role
special: couple, effects
traditional: comedies, couple, people, role
young: actor, couple, people, student

2
1 big influence   2 young couple   3 mainstream success
4 romantic comedies   5 special effects   6 bad mood

6
1 portrait   2 entertainers   3 reggae   4 flamenco
5 orchestra   6 Romeo+Juliet   7 magician   8 awful
9 new   10 choir   11 espresso
PERFORMANCE

Unit 3

3a (pages 20 and 21)

1
1 c   2 a

2
1 B   2 H   3 W   4 H   5 W   6 W   7 H   8 B

3
1 saw   2 best moment   3 solve the problem
4 amount of work you have to do
5 increased by twice as much   6 was successful

4
1 When did the sports fishermen see some oceanic whitetips?
2 When did Brian Skerry spot a shark?
3 How did he know that it was a whitetip?
4 What were Skerry and his assistant going after at the end of the assignment?
5 What happened on the eighth day?
6 What was Skerry doing when the weather improved?

5
1 saw … were surfing
2 was climbing … dropped
3 was … was coming up … were jumping
4 started … were filming
5 got … packed up … went
6 were sailing … got

6a
1 got   2 knew   3 flew   4 dealt   5 put   6 swam
7 saw   8 fell

6b
knew, flew
dealt, fell

7
underwater: diving, scuba diving
on the water: canoeing, jet-skiing, kayaking, rafting, rowing, parasailing, sailing, surfing, water polo, water-skiing, windsurfing
both: fishing, snorkelling, swimming, synchronised swimming

3b (pages 22 and 23)

1
1 iceberg   2 submarine   3 yacht   4 rocks   5 cannon
6 shipwreck

2
1 a

3
All the words – except *tornado* and *waves* – are in the programme.

4
1 a   2 b   3 c   4 c

5
1 bridges had disappeared – water
2 farmland had turned into desert – wind
3 rivers had changed course – water
4 roads had disappeared – water
5 sand had moved to new areas – wind
6 trees had washed away – water

6
1 most residents had left the area
2 at what had happened
3 there had been trees

4 roads and bridges had disappeared
5 where people had had farms
6 how much had changed

7
1 managed   2 were   3 had become   4 had already died
5 managed   6 had tried

8
1 d   2 b   3 c   4 e   5 a   *or*   1 d   2 c   3 e   4 b   5 a

3c (page 24)

1
Italy

2
1 from an underground water reserve
2 to extract the water, bottle it and sell it as drinking water
3 He had written a letter to the newspaper about banning bottled water.
4 The town decided to become 'bottled water free'.
5 after national and international newspapers wrote articles about the story

3
1 they didn't want to buy their own water in bottles
2 fight the water company … ban bottled water completely
3 had gone 'plastic bag free'
4 is 300 times greater than tap water
5 they can get it from the tap

4
1 become   2 met   3 received   4 obtain

5
1 d   2 b   3 f   4 e   5 a   6 c

3d (page 25)

1
1 During   2 After   3 suddenly   4 While   5 later   6 then

2
1 when   2 As   3 While   4 As   5 when   6 As

3e (page 26)

1
1 a   2 h   3 m   4 d   5 i   6 g   7 o   8 f   9 k   10 l   11 j
12 e   13 b   14 n   15 c

2a
1 arrived in   2 sad   3 met some friends   4 full of people
5 went   6 amazing   7 exciting   8 emotional   9 starting

2b
1 spectacular   2 bumped into   3 packed   4 made my way   5 familiar faces   6 tragic

3
1 fabulous, impressive, magnificent, spectacular
2 electrifying, exciting, exhilarating, thrilling
3 busy, crowded, full, packed
4 move on, set off, take off, travel

4
Model answer:
On the Saturday evening we all got dressed up and went to dinner in the spectacular dining room. The whole thing was a recreation of dinner on *Titanic*. The dining room was packed and it was thrilling to see everyone in authentic costumes. We bumped into some people we had met earlier and they joined our group. The food was amazing too and the whole thing was very moving.

Wordbuilding / Learning skills / Check! (page 27)

1
1 completely, definitely, easily, extremely, fast, fortunately, normally, quickly, seriously, slowly, unexpectedly, unpleasantly, unsuccessfully

2
1 easily, fast, quickly, slowly
2 Fortunately
3 extreme, fortunate, normal, serious, slow, unpleasant, unsuccessful
4 completely, definitely, unexpectedly
5 unsuccessful
6 definitely, quickly, slowly, unexpectedly

3
The student includes the following things:
example sentences; how he/she feels about something; other students; reminders to do things; test scores; vocabulary; writing (entry for 10 Nov)

4
because they are important

6
1 rain   2 bottled   3 fresh   4 running   5 hot   6 boiling
7 salt   8 cold

X	F	L	H	H	N	I	E	K	O
H	R	I	R	U	N	N	I	N	G
A	E	B	S	E	L	A	Z	B	I
R	S	O	Q	V	O	B	U	O	T
E	H	I	P	N	H	O	T	Y	S
O	A	L	Z	I	P	T	E	W	A
R	A	I	N	W	A	T	E	R	L
P	L	N	I	E	U	L	T	T	T
E	B	G	S	U	A	E	N	B	O
Y	U	V	C	O	L	D	X	R	U

Unit 4
4a (pages 28 and 29)

1
Speaker 1: education
Speaker 2: home, work
Speaker 3: health
Speaker 4: environment, languages

2
1 S   2 S   3 S   4 NS   5 S   6 NS   7 NS   8 NS

3
1 will   2 won't   3 will   4 definitely (*also* certainly)
5 certainly (*also* definitely)

4
1 probably   2 might (*also* could, may)   3 could (*also* may, might)   4 may (*also* could, might)   5 could (*also* may, might)

5
1 a   2 b   3 a   4 b

7
1 exciting, glamorous   2 dangerous, demanding
3 responsible, routine   4 rewarding, satisfying

8
1 jobs   2 working   3 work   4 jobs   5 work   6 job

9
a

4b (pages 30 and 31)

1
1 leave school   2 stay on at school   3 pass an exam
4 resit an exam   5 go to university   6 become an apprentice
7 get a degree   8 drop out of college

2
1 café   2 waitress   3 work there   4 her twenties
5 single

3
1 Auckland, New Zealand
2 London
3 to let him know her plans
4 it's been brilliant, but she's not going to stay there forever

4
1 Lorna's brother is finishing school soon.
2 Lorna will be in Auckland in May or June.
3 She's going to look for a new job in Auckland.
4 She hasn't found somewhere to live in Auckland.
5 She might be able to stay with Brett.
6 She promises to take her brother a Chelsea football shirt.

5
1 Apprentices don't earn much, do they?
2 If that doesn't work out
3 I don't think that's such a good idea.
4 I feel like doing something new
5 I'll have to think about what I'm going to do
6 he's staying on next year to do another course
7 while I do some job-hunting

6
1 do you   2 chemistry   3 hair and make-up
4 the shopping   5 nothing   6 pottery

7
1 I'm starting my new job next week.
2 I'll meet you tonight.
3 We're moving house soon.
4 My friend is going to leave college.
5 My friend is doing an exam tomorrow.
6 I'll help you study.
7 I'll see you later.

8
1 miles   2 email   3 I'll   4 fail   5 oil   6 feel

4c (page 32)

1
1 flexi-time   2 pay rise   3 staff discounts   4 bonus
5 overtime   6 paid holiday

2
1 b   2 b   3 c

3
1 F   2 T   3 T   4 F   5 F   6 T

4
1 people who were born at the same time as the Internet
2 He doesn't believe in making plans. Plans are for
   old people.
3 If you don't have an open mind, you might miss
   an opportunity.
4 because both the Internet and the people in the
   programme are 21 years old

5a
1 a   2 b   3 b   4 a

4d (page 33)

1
1 well-organised   2 self-confident   3 independent
4 methodical   5 creative   6 conscientious

2
1 d   2 a   3 b   4 c

3
1 Would you mind *or* Do you mind
2 Would it be all right if *or* Would it be OK if
3 Could you *or* Can you
4 Is it OK to *or* Is it all right to (*also* Can I *or* Could I)
5 Would you *or* Will you
6 Can *or* Could

4e (page 34)

1a
c

1b
1 Dear Mr Brown,
2 I am writing in reply to your advertisement.
3 I enclose my application form.
4 I am an enthusiastic person and I enjoy working
   with people.
5 I have several years' experience in this area.
6 I am available for interview at any time.
7 I look forward to hearing from you.
8 Yours sincerely,

2
some experience in catering or retail
hard-working and good under pressure
authorised to work in the UK

3
Model answer:
Dear Mr Kapoor,
I am writing in reply to your advertisement ref 119/XG for
waiters. I attach my application form.
I am an enthusiastic and hard-working person, and I enjoy
working with people.
I have worked as a waiter both here in the UK and in my
home country, Portugal. I have several years' experience in
both restaurants and cafeterias.
I am available for interview at any time and available to
start work at once.
I look forward to hearing from you.
Yours sincerely,
Manuel Santos

Wordbuilding / Learning skills / Check! (page 35)

1
1 f   2 b   3 d   4 h   5 e   6 g   7 c   8 a

2
1 run out   2 come back   3 turn up   4 drop out
5 get off   6 settle down

4
Possible answers:
Job titles: ballerina, film star, fire fighter, footballer, pilot,
police officer, rock star, scientist, train driver, vet
Pay and conditions: badly paid, demanding, dirty, responsible,
rewarding, routine, satisfying, secure, stressful, well-paid
Describing jobs: boring, dangerous, exciting, glamorous
Job requirements: degree, experience, skills

5
1 new   2 ambition   3 intend   4 factory   5 college
6 hard-working
CHINA

Unit 5

5a (pages 36 and 37)

1
1 Travel   2 luggage   3 delays   4 local transport
5 Plan   6 trip   7 round-the-world trip

2
1 trip   2 travelled   3 journeys   4 trips   5 journey   6 travel

3
1 d   2 c   3 a   4 b   5 e

4
1 a, b   2 a   3 b, c   4 a, c

5
1 be a big fan   2 come up laughing   3 be addicted to
4 see things from a fresh angle

6
1 has worked   2 has written   3 took   4 hasn't had
5 had   6 has been

7
1 Have (you) done   2 've/have been   3 haven't been
4 did (you) go   5 went   6 've/have always wanted
7 saw   8 've/have seen   9 flew   10 were   11 looked

5b (pages 38 and 39)

1
1 crowded, busy, vibrant   2 relaxing   3 peaceful,
remote   4 safe   5 exotic/unspoilt/tropical beaches, exotic
scenery   6 tropical/unspoilt

2
Monument Valley – western
Prague – action
London – romance

3
You can:
2 go on a tour with a local guide in Monument Valley
3 go up in a hot-air balloon in Monument Valley
5 go sightseeing in the Old Town in Prague
6 take a walking tour in London

4
1 since the 1930s
2 for generations
3 to take a hot-air balloon trip
4 in the 1990s
5 airlines have been adding more flights and more
  connections
6 one of the Harry Potter films

5
1 've/have been walking … 've/have seen
2 has been telling … 's/has met
3 've/have been taking … 's/has just run out
4 've/have been waiting … 've/have paid
5 've/have been exploring … 've/have found
6 haven't had … 've/have been sightseeing

6
1 I've been lying on the beach all day.
2 We've been travelling since seven. *or* We've been
  travelling for eight hours.
3 We've been coming here for ten years.
4 I've been reading this book since I arrived.
5 I've driven 1,000 kilometres.
6 We've stayed in three different hotels.

7
1 How long have you been lying on the beach? All day.
2 How long have you been travelling? Since seven o'clock.
  or For eight hours.

3 How long have you been coming here? For ten years.
4 How long have you been reading that book? Since I
  arrived.

5c (page 40)

1
All the words – except *extinct* and *tax* – are in the
audioscript.

2
1 driving   2 cruise   3 eco-tourist

3
1 b   2 a   3 a

4
1 a issues, projects   b habitats, species
2 a waste   b eco-friendly   c impact

5
1 d   2 a   3 c   4 b

6
1 and things   2 a few things   3 worst thing
4 sort of thing   5 best thing   6 important thing

5d (page 41)

1
1 baggage allowance   2 boarding card   3 car hire
4 food poisoning   5 hotel room   6 passport control
7 travel documents   8 train timetable

2
1 train timetable   2 passport control   3 hotel room
4 boarding cards   5 baggage allowance   6 food
poisoning   7 car hire   8 travel documents

3
1 b   2 f   3 e   4 c   5 a   6 d

4
1 at, at   2 from, from   3 for, For

5e (page 42)

1a
1 no way   2 wow   3 cool   4 awesome

1b
1 thx   2 oxox   3 LOL   4 BF   5 GF

1c
2 The beach is gorgeous!
3 The journey was exhausting!
5 I love it here!

1d
1 The food here is delicious.
2 I've been on a bumpy camel ride.
3 I've never been so hot in my life!
4 I'm taking it easy today because I did too much
  yesterday.
5 You'll find photos in the usual place online.

1e
1 Weather here fantastic.
2 Lying by the hotel pool since we arrived.
3 Thinking of staying an extra week cos it's so beautiful.
4 Have arranged to go on a couple of day trips.
5 Had a terrible flight. Long delay, seats uncomfortable
  and no food!

2
Model answer:
Hi Sue!
Had a terrible flight. Long delay, seats uncomfortable and no
food! But, anyway, the weather here is fantastic. Never been

so hot in my life! Hotel great – been lying by the hotel pool since we arrived. People seem lovely and food here delicious! Thinking of staying an extra week cos it's so beautiful.
Love,
Milla

Wordbuilding / Learning skills / Check! (page 43)

1
Accommodation: budget hotel, campsite, guest house, youth hostel
Things to pack: hand luggage, insect repellent, money belt, sun cream, travel tablets
At the airport: arrivals hall, baggage reclaim, departure lounge

2
1 travel tablet   2 insect repellent   3 youth hostel
4 campsite   5 arrivals hall   6 hand luggage
7 money belt   8 sun cream

3
1 trip, trip   2 travel, travelled, travel

4
1 tour   2 voyage   3 journey   4 voyage

5
1 delays   2 holidaymakers   3 habitats   4 mosquito
5 surfing   6 ticket   7 eco-tourism   8 destination

Unit 6

6a (pages 44 and 45)

1
natural: avocado, peanuts, prawns, steak
made from other ingredients: cheese, cheese snacks, pizza, popcorn

2
2 up your mind   3 them a nice meal   4 simple steak
5 suggestion   6 me hungry

3
a simple steak   b a suggestion   c them a nice meal
d me hungry   e up your mind

4
1 make lunch   2 make a mess   3 makes me ill
4 make you a drink   5 make sense   6 make up my mind

5
1 north   2 Aboriginal people   3 edible   4 collecting

6
ants, grass, water lilies

7
c

8
1 You can't (or You mustn't) camp in the park.
2 You have to picnic in designated areas.
3 You can't (or You mustn't) swim in the rivers.
4 You should carry water with you.
5 You have to inform the warden in advance of your visit.
6 You don't have to show identification on entry.
7 You shouldn't approach wild animals.
8 You have to report any accidents or incidents with wild animals.

6b (pages 46 and 47)

2
1 a goal   2 individuals   3 resolutions   4 intrepid
5 challenges   6 a platform

3
1 Jodi Cobb   2 Børge Ousland   3 Robert D. Ballard

4
1 If you make a healthy meal, you'll feel better afterwards.
2 If I watch a movie, I'll enjoy myself.
3 If you find a new route to work, you'll save money.
4 If you take chewing gum with you, you won't / will not smoke.
5 If you don't buy chocolate, you won't eat it.
6 You'll live longer if you have a good diet.

5
1 You won't achieve anything unless you take risks.
2 Your friends will help you as soon as you ask them.
3 You'll be successful when you plan things carefully.
4 You won't know what you can do until you try.
5 You'll make a lot of mistakes before you succeed.
6 You won't save any money if you don't have a plan.

6
not part of a healthy lifestyle: cutting down on relaxation, avoiding outdoor activities, taking up smoking

7
1 b   2 d   3 c   4 a

6c (page 48)

1
1 electric   2 high   3 indoor   4 night   5 irregular

2
1 c   2 a   3 b   4 b   5 c   6 b

3
a

4a
1 adjective   2 adverb   3 adjective   4 adjective   5 verb

4b
1 difficult e   2 far b   3 long a   4 badly c   5 quickly f
6 soon d

6d (page 49)

1
1 What's that made from?
2 What do they taste like?
3 I think I'll try that.
4 Does it come with vegetables?
5 I'll have the same.

2
1 need to   2 don't need to   3 have to   4 have to
5 don't need to

3
1 baked   2 fish   3 hot   4 bland

4
1 D   2 S   3 M   4 S

5a
1 comfortable   2 evening   3 national   4 travelling

5b
beverage   camera   poisoning   several   snorkelling

6e (page 50)

1a
1 opening times   2 prices   3 cafeteria

1b
1 The swimming pool doesn't open until 9 a.m., therefore people can't go swimming before they go to work.

2 Taking away the discounts for retired people means that they can't afford to use the centre very often.
3 The multi-ticket scheme is too complicated. Consequently, people don't take advantage of offers.
4 Opening the cafeteria to the public will result in more people using the centre.
5 The price increase has led to fewer families using the centre now.

2
Model answer:
Dear Sir,
We are writing to express our concern at the recent changes to Newton Fitness Centre. We are concerned about three aspects of these changes: prices, opening times and the cafeteria.
In our view, the multi-ticket scheme is too complicated. Consequently, people don't take advantage of offers. The price increase has led to fewer families using the centre now. We also note that taking away the discounts for retired people means that they can't afford to use the centre very often.
In addition, the swimming pool doesn't open until 9 a.m., therefore people can't go swimming before they go to work. Finally, we feel that opening the cafeteria to the public will result in more people using the centre.
We request that you review these changes to the services that the fitness centre provides to local residents.
Yours sincerely
PH Singh
Newton Residents' Association

Wordbuilding / Learning skills / Check! (page 51)

1
1 gone up   2 put up   3 take up   4 speed up   5 grow up

2
1 come down   2 get ... down   3 slow down
4 take ... down   5 bring down

3
1 writing the same idea in different ways
2 thinking about who the reader is
3 listing useful linking words

6
1 durian   2 junk food   3 caffeine   4 raw   5 plantain
6 English   7 blue   8 stilton

Unit 7

7a (pages 52 and 53)

1
The article mentions *veranda* and *attic*.

2
1 You can find longhouses all over the world, from northern Europe across Asia and also in the Americas.
2 In Indonesia, the space under the longhouse is for animals. In Viking longhouses, there was a special section at one end for animals.
3 Either on a central fire or in an annexe.
4 The Asian longhouse is still built today in tropical areas.

3
1 longer   2 most appropriate   3 best   4 crowded
5 more easily   6 better   7 hotter   8 closer   9 warmer
10 hotter   11 less exposed   12 more private
13 more sophisticated

4
1 more and more popular   2 higher and higher
3 faster and faster   4 The bigger ... the brighter
5 The closer ... the better   6 The nicer ... the more often

5
1 The longhouse was one of the most widespread home designs.
2 Ceiling fans use a lot less electricity than air conditioning.
3 The rent is slightly higher than we expected.
4 This is by far the best house we've seen today.
   (*also* This is the best house by far we've seen today.)
5 A veranda makes a house look a bit more inviting.
6 The room is far cosier when the fire is lit.

7b (pages 54 and 55)

1
1 modern   2 neighbourhood   3 public transport
4 atmosphere   5 built-up   6 polluted   7 skyscraper
8 residents   9 traffic   10 run-down   11 open spaces

2
Used to can replace the past simple in sentences 1, 2, 4 and 6.

3
1 This area didn't use to have so many skyscrapers (before).
2 The pollution here used to be much worse than it is now.
4 The atmosphere didn't use to be so relaxed (in the past).
6 There didn't use to be as many crowded neighbourhoods.

4
Would can replace used to in sentences 2 and 6.

5
1 When I was young, we lived next to my school.
2 My friends and I would play in the street.
3 There was a lot of traffic along this road.
4 I didn't like my neighbours.
5 A huge tree grew in front of our house.
6 We wouldn't go out if it was raining.

7
1, 3 and 4 are true.
2 Timbuktu is a World Heritage Site now.
5 It was invaded in the 16th century.

8
1 learning   2 collection   3 law   4 location   5 river
6 Camel   7 gold   8 scholars

7c (page 56)

1
1 Tokyo   2 Dhaka   3 Mumbai   4 Sao Paulo   5 Delhi

2
The name refers to 19 cities that will have more than 20 million people in the 21st century.

3
1 b, c   2 a, b   3 a, b

4
1 Tokyo   2 Lagos   3 Mumbai   4 Los Angeles

7d (page 57)

1
1 walking *or* to walk   2 to stay   3 prefer
4 watching ... reading   5 have   6 'd prefer

2
Possible answers:
2 d I prefer swimming because going to the gym is too tiring.
3 g I'd rather / I prefer to / I'd prefer to have one long holiday because you can travel further.
4 c I'd prefer a job nearer home because commuting is very expensive.

5 e I'd rather / I'd prefer to / I prefer to rent than buy because I'm not sure if I'll stay here.
6 f I prefer reading the news online as it's more up-to-date.
7 a I prefer small shops because big stores are less friendly.
8 h I prefer driving a small car as it uses less petrol.

7e (page 58)

1
1 e   2 d   3 a   4 g   5 b   6 f   7 c

2
1 e, g   2 a, d   3 b, c, f

3a
1 as = because
2 like = such as

3b
1 As   2 like   3 As   4 like   5 as   6 like

Wordbuilding / Learning skills / Check! (page 59)

1
1 relaxing   2 walking   3 entertaining   4 growing
5 overhanging   6 filling   7 rising   8 ageing
9 refreshing   10 winding

2
1 dining room   2 bedroom   3 kitchen   4 sitting room
5 bedroom   6 kitchen / bathroom   7 kitchen   8 bathroom

3
1 A   2 V   3 V   4 A   5 V   6 N

4
1 N   2 A   3 N   4 V   5 V   6 A

6
1 New York   2 estate agent   3 igloo   4 ger   5 habitat
6 brick   7 outside   8 urban   9 rent   10 skyscrapers
NEIGHBOURS

Unit 8

8a (pages 60 and 61)

1
1 fish; near Tasmania, Australia; handfish have fins which look like hands and they use them to walk along the ocean floor
2 bat; Papua New Guinea; it resembles Yoda in the *Star Wars* films
3 worm; in the sea around the Philippines; it looks like a squid (because it has tentacles on its head) and a worm (because its body is divided into segments)

2
1 a C   b C   c S
2 d C   e C   f S
3 g C   h S

3
1 ocean floor, seabed   2 specimen   3 species
4 predators   5 toxic   6 marine   7 segments

4
1 It must be a bird.
2 It might/could be a leaf/stem.
3 It must be a lake.
4 They must be spiders.
5 It might/could be a shark/whale.

5
1 look like   2 Look   3 looks as though   4 looks

6
1 e   2 b   3 a   4 c   5 d

8b (pages 62 and 63)

1
moai = statue   *pukao* = 'hat'

2
1 more than 800
2 human figures
3 stone
4 carved out of volcanic stone
5 over a period of 600 years, ending 400 years ago
6 no – only some of them

3
1 F   2 T   3 F   4 F

4
1 must have   2 must have   3 may have   4 must have
5 must have

5
1 may have seen   2 can't have been   3 must have seen
4 must have been   5 can't have been   6 must have had
7 might have been   8 might have been
9 could have phoned

7
1 century, period   2 beliefs, traditions
3 ancient, prehistoric, sacred   4 fragments, pieces
5 ancestors, society

8
1 c   2 e   3 d   4 b   5 a

8c (page 64)

1
Wallabies are eating poppies and then becoming so disoriented that they run around in the fields erratically, creating paths that resemble crop circles.

2
2 extraterrestrial   3 physical   4 wallabies   5 wallabies
6 poppies   7 wallabies   8 poppies   9 wallabies
10 humans   11 patterns   12 hoaxers   13 tools   14 patterns

3
b, c

4
1 b   2 c   3 a

8d (page 65)

1
The first two stories are true. The third story is almost true. The last story was what the author's friend told her mum in 1971 and was believed!

2
1 off   2 right   3 mistake   4 joking   5 having … on
6 sure

8e (page 66)

1a
c

1b
c struck   d called, started   b responded, happened
a was, cut off, said

2
1 temporarily   2 immediately   3 fortunately
4 extremely   5 quickly   6 incredibly

3
1 really   2 Luckily   3 briefly   4 unbelievably
5 instantly   6 rapidly

4
1 Incredibly, nobody knows what happened.
2 Sadly, this is not the first time this has happened.
3 The car was deliberately damaged.
4 The man spoke sadly about the incident.
5 Things are gradually returning to normal.
6 We were incredibly shocked by the news.

Wordbuilding / Learning skills / Check! (page 67)

1
1 adventurous   2 ancestral   3 archaeological   4 beneficial
5 central   6 courageous   7 factual   8 famous
9 financial   10 glamorous   11 global   12 historical
13 humorous   14 industrial   15 natural   16 nutritious
17 physical

2
1 nutritious   2 courageous   3 archaeological   4 factual
5 global   6 industrial

3
1 c   2 e   3 d   4 a   5 b

4
1 Where did it happen?
2 When did it happen?
3 Who is involved?
4 What happened exactly?
5 How did it happen?
6 Why did it happen?

5
1 There is enough information to answer all the
   questions.
   1 the north of Taiwan
   2 October
   3 environmentalists, students, campaigners
   4 Frogs are increasingly under threat as humans move
     into their habitat.
   5 A wildlife group monitors the road with the help of local
     students.
   6 to avoid frog deaths
2 There is enough information to answer all the questions.
   1 Holland
   2 this month
   3 producers
   4 an unusual new ice cream has been created
   5 the main ingredient is camel's milk
   6 Camel's milk has less fat and more vitamins than
     normal milk.

6
1 spider   2 ant   3 Arctic tern   4 monkey   5 beetle
PARROT

Unit 9

9a (pages 68 and 69)

1
1 receipt   2 bill   3 change   4 bank statement
5 debit card   6 bank transfer

2
1 The passwords mentioned are for online banking and
   cash machines, and to access email accounts.
2 A password should be unique and secret.
3 Mark Burnett is a security expert.
4 They are the ten most commonly used passwords in
   the world.

3
1 the   2 –   3 –   4 a   5 your   6 your   7 your
8 the   9 all   10 –   11 their   12 a   13 the   14 the   15 the
16 your   17 your   18 a

4a
1 each other   2 yourselves   3 each other   4 each other
5 each other   6 themselves

4b
1 himself   2 myself   3 each other   4 herself   5 himself
6 each other

5a
1 himself   2 reflected   3 and   4 beautiful   5 his   6 looked

6
1 lend   2 borrow   3 lent   4 lend   5 borrow   6 lent

9b (pages 70 and 71)

1
1 a, b   2 a, b   3 a, c   4 c

2
1 c   2 b   3 a   4 c   5 b

3
1 are being assembled   2 contains   3 will be bought
4 have been made   5 are used   6 include
7 has often been associated   8 are being substituted

4
1 lovely = opinion, plain = factual, gold = factual
2 beautiful = opinion, traditional = factual, hand-woven =
   factual
3 gorgeous = opinion, antique = factual, silk = factual
4 nice = opinion, silver = factual

5
1 large, tiny   2 19th century, old
3 hand-made, mass-produced   4 blue   5 Italian
6 plastic, wool

6
1 The factory makes mass-produced plastic toys.
2 It's a 19th century silk wall hanging.
3 We bought a blue wool rug in the sale.
4 She usually wears large gold earrings.
5 It's a tiny Italian box.
6 We've got some old plastic chairs in the garden.

9c (page 72)

2
1 b   2 a   3 c

3
1 a   2 b, →   3 b, ←   4 →   5 →   6 b, ←   7 c, ←
8 c, ←

4
1 How much did it cost you?
2 I've spent far too much money today.
3 This shirt is much nicer.
4 How much of this paper do you need?
5 She always uses too much perfume, I think.
6 I haven't had much time to go shopping recently.
7 Oh, that's much too expensive!
8 I can get this much cheaper online.

9d (page 73)

1
1 Can I look at one?
2 Is it in the sale?
3 I want something more modern.
4 Yes. Can I bring it back if my brother doesn't like it?
5 Do you work in the dining room section?
6 Have you got the reference number?
7 How much do you charge?
8 Yes, you can pay by card or in cash.

2
1 in stock   2 tills   3 exchange   4 delivery
5 reference number   6 receipt … return

9e (page 74)

1a
Nissan Micra: four years old; metallic blue, 3-door
hatchback, petrol engine; 4,500 euros
Canon EOS: black, digital SLR camera, HD movie mode,
12 MP, 18–55 mm lens, never used (unwanted gift); 550 euros
Leather sofa: chocolate brown leather, Italian design,
3-seater; very comfortable
Information that is not relevant:
need payment quickly
our first purchase when married!

1b
Extra information:
The car has been serviced regularly at Nissan
authorised garages.
It is in excellent condition.

2
Model answers:
For sale
Brand new Canon EOS digital SLR camera. 12 MP and
comes with 18–55 mm lens. Also has HD movie mode. The
camera and lens are black. Excellent condition. This camera
was an unwanted gift and has never been used. Carrying
case also included in price: 550 euros.

For sale
Italian design leather sofa. The sofa is 3-seater and a stylish
chocolate-brown colour. Very comfortable and easy to keep
clean. Excellent price of 400 euros.

Wordbuilding / Learning skills / Check! (page 75)

1
1 world-famous actor, brand, street
2 sweet-smelling flowers, lemons
3 lethal-looking knife, weapon
4 hand-dyed leather, silk
5 eight-year-old boy, child

2
1 paper   2 Hand   3 locally   4 solar   5 vacuum   6 old

3
Possible answers:
borrow: b, c, d
merchant: b, c
mass-produced: a, c, d

5
a coins   b receipt   c earrings   d spices   e till   f rug
g orange juice   h mobile
CUSTOMER

Unit 10

10a (pages 76 and 77)

1
1 Body Heat   2 Cold Water   3 Hot Air
4 High Altitude   5 Diving Deep   6 Lack of Oxygen
7 Blood Loss   8 Starvation   9 Dehydration

2
1 45 days   2 7 days   3 10 minutes   4 40 per cent
5 42°C   6 bigger lungs and more red blood cells

3
1 b That's the patient I read about.
2 d This is a new kidney which was grown in a laboratory.
3 c Cosmetic surgery is a medical procedure which can
      be expensive.
4 e I talked to the surgeon who operated on me.
5 f That's the hospital where they do heart transplants.
6 a That was the day when I came out of hospital.

5
1 This operation, which is performed frequently, is
   not dangerous.
2 The nurse, who explained everything to me, was
   very professional.
3 The injection, which the nurse gives me, doesn't hurt.
4 My ankle, which I broke last year, has completely healed.
5 Our doctor, who is very young, is very knowledgeable.

6
1 a   2 c   3 c   4 a   5 c   6 b

10b (pages 78 and 79)

1 had to … you go
2 could take … would be
3 would you miss … would be
4 moved … would be
5 would find … went … would welcome … would probably
   do … would have to
6 would be … would love … had

2
1 would   2 couldn't   3 would   4 could   5 would
6 might   7 would   8 might

3
1 Would you go   2 'd/would be   3 wouldn't go
4 paid   5 weren't   6 'd/would love   7 'll/will probably
get   8 drops   9 'll/will buy   10 'll/will never happen

4
1 clothes   2 car technology   3 food   4 air conditioning
5 daily routine

5
1 woman   2 woman   3 woman   4 woman   5 man
6 man

6
1 wouldn't enjoy: man
2 'd/would feel … wore: woman
3 lived … 'd/would get: woman
4 'd/would avoid … got up: woman

7
1 d   2 a   3 b   4 c

10c (page 80)

1
b

2
Both the film and the photo are about brain activity/power.

3
1 They look at how films deal with science.
2 The main idea of the film is that we only use 20 per cent of
   our brain power.
3 The main character takes a special pill that lets him use
   100 per cent of his brain power.
4 He writes a book. He learns to speak Italian. He becomes
   a master of martial arts.

4
1 true   2 functions   3 hidden   4 inefficient   5 limitless

5

The three things the character did are things which we could all manage to do – if we used our own limitless brain power more efficiently.

6

1 b   2 a   3 d

7

1 invite   2 steal   3 lead   4 borrow   5 carry   6 react
7 travel   8 have

8

1 h   2 d   3 e   4 a   5 f   6 c   7 g   8 b

10d (page 81)

1

1 He's been stung by a wasp.
2 She's cut herself / her finger.
3 He's fallen off his skateboard.
4 He's got food poisoning.
5 He's fallen off the wall.
6 She's tripped up.

2

1 b, f   2 c, e, f   3 c, f   4 a, e   5 a, c, e, f   6 a, c, d, e, f

3

1 d   2 f   3 b   4 g   5 c   6 e   7 a

4

You can use these beginnings with all of the suggestions except *ignore*. The verb is in the infinitive.
If I were you; I would; You should; You'd better;
Why don't you
For example:
get it looked at; go to A&E; keep an eye on it; put some antihistamine cream on it
You can use these beginnings with all of the suggestions except *ignore*. The verb is in the *-ing* form.
It might be worth; You're best; Have you tried
For example:
getting it X-rayed; going to see the doctor; putting cream on it; washing it
I wouldn't goes logically with *ignore*:
I wouldn't ignore it.

5

1 quick and easy   2 name and address   3 big and small
4 black and white   5 nice and friendly   6 young and old

10e (page 82)

1a

Incorrect options: 1 However; 2 All the same; 3 Actually; 4 By the way, Incidentally; 5 before I forget

1b

He's asking Jack if he should take part in an ultramarathon. He asks Jack because Jack knows him better than anyone.

1c

1 of course
2 By the way, Incidentally, To be honest
3 Anyway, In fact, Naturally, Obviously, Of course, Well
4 Anyway, Even so, Of course

2

1 I don't know what I would do in your position.
2 Even so, if you have the right training, you can do it.
3 As I understand it, you will do the race next year if you decide to do it.
4 That will give you plenty of time to prepare and to see if it is a good idea.

5 I'm sure you won't regret it.
6 By the way, we'll probably call in and visit you next month, if we go to Scotland.

3

Model answer:
Hi Ali
I'm sorry it's taken me a while to reply to your email. I've been thinking about what you said, of course!
To be honest, I've never been faced with this kind of situation, so I don't know what I would do in your position. You are the only person who knows what your body is capable of. Obviously, doing a race like that is going to be a massive challenge. Even so, if you have the right training you can do it.
As I understand it, you will do the race next year if you decide to do it. That will give you plenty of time to prepare and to see if it is a good idea or not. It seems like a great opportunity, so if I was you I would seriously consider it. Well, it's up to you in the end. I'm sure you won't regret it, though.
By the way, we'll probably call in and visit you next month if we go to Scotland. I'll let you know a couple of days in advance. If you haven't made up your mind, we can talk about the ultramarathon a bit more then.
Regards
Jack

Wordbuilding / Learning skills / Check! (page 83)

1

1 beautiful   2 breathless   3 careful / careless
4 cheerful   5 colourful / colourless   6 graceful
7 harmful / harmless   8 lifeless   9 peaceful
10 powerful / powerless   11 resourceful   12 respectful
13 stressful   14 successful   15 tuneful / tuneless
16 useful / useless

2

1 careful   2 graceful   3 stressful   4 resourceful
5 harmless   6 useless

6

Possible answers:
1 an insect which can sting you
2 something a mosquito could do to you
3 something which could cut you
4 a person who treats illness
5 a person who has to leave their home because of war
6 a race which is 26 miles (42 kilometres) long
7 a person who travels in space

Unit 11

11a (pages 84 and 85)

1

1 sports pages   2 business section   3 world news
4 national news   5 comment and analysis
6 entertainment   7 politics and society   8 front page

2

1 Richard Leakey is a legendary conservationist.
2 Paula Kahumbu is the current director of WildlifeDirect.

3

1 c   2 b   3 c   4 c   5 b

4

When Rosy grew blind and stopped mating, the website published his story. People then donated enough money to perform cataract surgery, which successfully replaced his lenses, and now he is practically back to a normal life.

5
1 The presenter said (that) good news never made the headlines.
2 Jo Makeba said (that) we could publish our own photos directly onto the Internet.
3 The presenter asked what exactly WildlifeDirect was.
4 Jo Makeba said (that) Richard had set up WildlifeDirect.
5 Paula Kahumbu said (that) the website had published Rosy's story.
6 The presenter asked if he could see him on the WildlifeDirect site.

6
1 You said (that) you didn't watch the news.
2 You told me (that) you knew how to upload photos.
3 You asked me if I had seen that programme before.
4 You said (that) the documentary had just finished.
5 You said (that) you would tell me when the news came on.
6 You asked me if I could help you download that video.

7
1 b   2 d   3 f   4 a   5 c   6 e

11b (pages 86 and 87)

1
1 a   2 f, g   3 b, d   4 e   5 c

2
1 While phones could talk to phones, and computers could talk to computers, you couldn't send a simple text message between the two systems.
2 He wrote the software that allows phones and computers to communicate with each other.
3 If you download the free software online, you won't need to use the Internet.
4 Any organisation that wants to use text messaging can use it.

3
economical, freely available, reliable, simple

4
1 signal   2 network   3 send a text message
4 internet connection   5 write software   6 cable
7 downloading … online   8 keyboard   9 contact list
10 launch a website

5
1 Ken Banks promised he would find a solution.
2 The company invited Ken Banks to tell them about his ideas.
3 The phone company offered to give all their customers ten free texts.
4 The website asked the public to donate text messages.
5 The doctor told the patients not to be late for appointments.
6 The officials reminded all hospitals to make arrangements for their visits the following week.

6
1 didn't realise … couldn't   2 didn't know … worked
3 thought … could   4 wondered … 'd/had sent

11c (page 88)

1
1 teen   2 three   3 87

2
who, three, salt, name, give, stand, new, yellow, I, two, five

3
1 T   2 T   3 F   4 F   5 T

4
The computer takes a lot less time to look at the data. It also highlights patterns that might be difficult to see.

5
1 c   2 a   3 b, c

6
1 Time   2 great time   3 have time   4 time
5 difficult time   6 time and time again   7 spend time
8 modern times

11d (page 89)

1
a This is a message for Nils Davis. A
b I'm afraid Dan's in a meeting.
c It's about the delivery of phone chargers. A
d My name's Jill and I'm on 07956841. A
e Can I take a message?
f Yes, who's calling?
g I'll try and call you later. A
h I'll let him know that you rang.

2
1 b   2 e   3 f   4 h

3a
1 I … you   2 you … me   3 you … your   4 you … me your
5 him   6 her

11e (page 90)

1
1 b   2 a   3 –   4 c   5 a, b

2
1 It was agreed that the party would finish at midnight.
2 It was decided that we would decorate the street. / It was decided that the street would be decorated.
3 It was suggested that we should put up a marquee. / It was suggested that a marquee should be put up.
4 It was explained that no special permission was needed for this type of event.
5 It was reported that preparations were complete.

3
Model answer:
Street Party meeting 28 February
Twenty five residents came to the meeting to discuss the street party.
The first item on the agenda was the time and date. It was agreed that the party would be on 30 April and would start at 2 p.m.
The next thing to be discussed were the preparations.
Ms Clarke said she had contacted a DJ about the music.
Ms Gregg said she would organise the food. She asked volunteers to sign up on the list. Mr and Mrs Walker offered to organise the street decorations. This will include lights, flags and balloons, and so on.
Mr Blair asked if we would need a licence for party. He will check this.
Finally, the date of the next meeting was fixed as 21 March at 8 p.m. at the community centre.

Wordbuilding / Learning skills / Check! (page 91)

1
unfortunately, unpleasantly = adverbs

2
1 b   2 b   3 a   4 a   5 b   6 b   7 b   8 b

5
1 translators   2 dictionaries   3 vocabulary practice
4 grammar practice   5 practice exams

6

1 text 2 twitter 3 software 4 footage 5 headline
6 news 7 viral 8 signal

W	T	L	R	G	O	P	E	T	E
H	E	A	D	L	I	N	E	V	Y
C	X	R	F	I	N	E	N	I	S
I	T	S	O	F	T	W	A	R	E
P	W	U	O	P	Z	S	V	A	A
R	S	K	T	T	I	A	E	L	S
L	C	A	A	L	L	Q	R	G	L
T	S	I	G	N	A	L	T	D	C
Q	B	G	E	N	M	U	K	F	T
U	O	Y	T	W	I	T	T	E	R

Unit 12

12a (pages 92 and 93)

1
1 b 2 a 3 d 4 e 5 c

2
1 As masses of people relocated throughout Cambodia, they
often created communities and farmland that affected
elephant habitat.
At the same time, with rain forests shrinking, hungry
elephants come onto farmland, destroying crops.
Desperately poor farmers fought back, killing elephants to
protect their land and livelihood.
2 They were essential in the construction of the Angkor Wat
temple and are depicted in honour on its walls.
3 When farmers were arrested for clearing the forest, they
could no longer feed their families.
(The government had still not established schools in
these areas and) farmers were very concerned that their
children could not read or write.

3
1 a, b 2 a, c 3 b, c 4 a, b 5 c

4
1 Cambodia's elephants could have died out completely.
2 In theory, the conflict between people and animals
shouldn't have happened.
3 The Cambodians couldn't have built Angkor Wat without
using elephants.
4 Conservation efforts should have re-established respect
for elephants.
5 Conservationists should have paid more attention to
human needs.
6 The government should have provided schools.

5
1 You should have studied harder.
2 Someone could have broken in.
3 He should have taken his tablets.
4 You should have bought a bigger one.
5 We couldn't have done it without her.
6 You should have used your GPS.

12b (pages 94 and 95)

1
1 c, h 2 f, i 3 a, d 4 e, g 5 b, j
1 If JK Rowling hadn't written the Harry Potter stories,
millions of boys wouldn't have got into books.
she wouldn't have become a millionaire.

2 If Tim Berners-Lee hadn't invented the Internet,
personal computers wouldn't have become so popular.
social networking wouldn't have been possible.
3 If Alexander Fleming hadn't discovered penicillin,
antibiotics wouldn't have been developed.
millions of people would have died from infections.
4 If Dian Fossey hadn't studied mountain gorillas,
most of them would have been killed.
she wouldn't have been murdered.
5 If Wangari Maathai hadn't won the Nobel Peace Prize,
many people wouldn't have heard of her.
thousands of Kenyan women wouldn't have had an income.

2
1 Millions of boys wouldn't have got into books if JK
Rowling hadn't written the Harry Potter stories.
JK Rowling wouldn't have become a millionaire if she
hadn't written the Harry Potter stories.
2 Personal computers wouldn't have become so popular if
Tim Berners-Lee hadn't invented the Internet.
Social networking wouldn't have been possible if Tim
Berners-Lee hadn't invented the Internet.
3 Antibiotics wouldn't have been developed if Alexander
Fleming hadn't discovered penicillin.
Millions of people would have died from infections if
Alexander Fleming hadn't discovered penicillin.
4 Most mountain gorillas would have been killed if Dian
Fossey hadn't studied them.
Dian Fossey wouldn't have been murdered if she hadn't
studied mountain gorillas.
5 Many people wouldn't have heard of Wangari Maathai if
she hadn't won the Nobel Peace Prize.
Thousands of Kenyan women wouldn't have had an income
if Wangari Maathai hadn't won the Nobel Peace Prize.

3
1 If JK Rowling hadn't become unemployed, she wouldn't
have started writing.
2 Tim Berners-Lee wouldn't have worked on hypertext if he
hadn't wanted to share information with other researchers.
3 If Alexander Fleming had cleaned his dishes, penicillin
wouldn't have grown on them.
4 Dian Fossey would never have gone to Africa if a friend
hadn't invited her on a safari.
5 If Wangari Maathai hadn't started the Green Belt movement,
millions of trees wouldn't have been planted in Kenya.

4
1 antibiotics, Fleming
2 Harry Potter films, JK Rowling
3 forward slashes after 'http', Tim Berners-Lee
4 Dian Fossey, her murder

5
1 a 2 b 3 b 4 b 5 a 6 a 7 b 8 b

12c (page 96)

1
c

2
1 polar bear, lion
2 chameleon, octopus
3 It squirts a cloud of black ink at the predator.
4 The octopus took it out of the jar.
5 The octopus got into their tank and ate them.
6 They saw a trail of water on the floor.

3
1 c 2 c 3 b

4
1 surfing 2 on 3 crazy 4 to 5 back 6 hungry
7 away 8 out

5

1 going for a walk   2 gone for lunch   3 going for a coffee
4 go for a run   5 go for a swim   6 go for a pizza

12d (page 97)

1

1 help MA   2 things AA   3 trouble MA   4 accident AA

2

1 e   2 c   3 f   4 b   5 a   6 d

4

1 Not only did you forget to ring me, but you also switched off your phone.
2 Not only did she lose my umbrella, but she also forgot to tell me.
3 Not only did he break my vase, but he also didn't apologise.
4 Not only did they arrive late, but they also brought uninvited guests.
5 Not only did the octopus work out how to get into the jar, but it also ate the prawn.
6 Not only did the scientist win the competition, but she also started a successful business.

12e (page 98)

1a

1 vocabulary   2 style   3 linking words   4 grammar
5 spelling   6 relevance

1b

1 photos/pictures, trip   2 He, His
3 although   4 would never have gone
5 families

2

g

3

a And finally, be patient with them when they speak English. If <u>you never try</u> to learn a language yourself, then <u>you try</u> taking a short course so that you know how it feels! (2)
b Find out if there is anything your student can't eat, either for religious reasons or because they really dislike a particular food item or <u>plate</u>. <u>I don't like eggs, for example</u>. (2)
c Make sure that you explain your household and family rules very clearly at the <u>begginning</u>. (1)
d Respect their privacy <u>in spite of</u> they are in your home. For the duration of their stay, their bedroom is <u>there</u> own private space. (2)
e Talk to your student about life in <u>the student's</u> own country. This helps you to anticipate what problems <u>the student</u> might have during <u>the student's</u> visit. (3)

f Treat the student as you would expect your own child to be treated if they <u>are</u> abroad. (1)
g We've had quite a few foreign students to stay <u>since</u> the last few years and each time it <u>was</u> been a different, but enjoyable, experience. If you're thinking about becoming a host family, here are a few tips for you. (2)
h You can ask your student to help with things <u>as</u> setting the table if that's what your own children do, but don't expect them to help you with the <u>homework</u>. (2)

4

Model answer:

Tips for host families

We've had quite a few foreign students to stay <u>in</u> the last few years and each time it <u>has</u> been a different, but enjoyable, experience. If you're thinking about becoming a host family, here are a few tips for you.
Treat the student as you would expect your own child to be treated if they <u>were</u> abroad.
Respect their privacy <u>even though</u> they are in your home. For the duration of their stay, their bedroom is <u>their</u> own private space.
Make sure that you explain your household and family rules very clearly at the <u>beginning</u>.
Find out if there is anything your student can't eat, either for religious reasons or because they really dislike a particular food item or <u>dish</u>.
You can ask your student to help with things <u>like</u> setting the table if that's what your own children do, but don't expect them to help you with <u>housework</u>.
Talk to your student about life in <u>their</u> own country. This helps you to anticipate what problems <u>they</u> might have during <u>their</u> visit.
And finally, be patient with them when they speak English. If <u>you've never tried</u> to learn a language yourself, then <u>you could</u> try taking a short course, so that you know how it feels!

Wordbuilding / Learning skills / Check! (page 99)

1

1 inaccurate   2 inconclusive   3 incredible   4 ineffective
5 inefficient   6 inexpensive   7 inexperienced   8 illegal
9 illogical   10 inoffensive   11 impatient   12 imperfect
13 impolite   14 impossible   15 improbable   16 intolerant

2

1 a   2 b   3 a   4 a   5 c   6 b

4

a backpack   b hammock   c tent   d sleeping bag
e sword   f sledge   g dried food
TRACKER

IELTs practice test

Listening

1 B they've got the full programme of events fixed now
2 A But I'm going to get tickets for the film
3 September The opening night is September 20th
4 0967 990776
5 (a/the) (local) bank there's a commercial sponsor – it's a local bank
6 (a/the) musical Like on Monday there's a musical in the City Hall
7 (the) sports centre but it's at the sports centre
8 poetry (evening) it's a poetry evening
9 (£)12.75 £12.75 for students
10 (the/some) fireworks just the fireworks in the city park
11 B come along at one o'clock any Wednesday. Spaces on the tour are limited to twenty-five
12 C teachers must … phone to agree a time in advance
13 A so college groups would pay £75 for the shorter tour
14 A though there is a small shop selling souvenirs
15 D There's also a lecture room which groups can book for an extra charge
16 1748 came to London to work … in 1748.
17 army 1760 … when he became a surgeon in the army
18 teaching museum gave the name 'teaching museum' to his collection
19 500 with 500 species of plants and animals represented
20 (the) government in 1799 the collection was purchased by the government
21 statement A statement of aims is the correct term
22 information sheet it's good to prepare an information sheet for participants
23 statistics/(statistical) data I want the project to have statistical data, not just to be a collection of opinions
24 C costs … as we don't have a budget, it's not something you need to include.
25 A I do need to know your criteria for choosing who to interview
26 B not essential at the proposal stage on this project, but … include them because it could save time later
27 C I'm going to be giving you a template to use, so there's no need to go into that in the proposal
28 A M: You only need a few, chosen randomly.
29 B Sarah: … twenty a day
    M: … at the end of each day's interviewing then
30 C I'll only use the information for my research – that I won't pass it on to anyone else … the only promise I'm making
31 135 covering an area of 135 square kilometres
32 (phosphate) mining the most significant economic activity is currently mining
33 bat have died out, as has one species of bat
34 14 the island's 14 crab species
35 Expert Working Group a report from the Expert Working Group it has set up
36 leaves the crabs' diet is largely made up of leaves
37 solitary alone in its burrow, and so is actually quite solitary
38 dry stays there most of the time, especially during the dry season
39 November it's usually sometime in November.
40 bridges even constructing bridges for the crabs

Reading

1 TRUE It covers online shopping … shopping by phone
2 TRUE you must get written confirmation of this information after you have made your purchase
3 TRUE you can get a refund if things aren't delivered on the agreed date
4 FALSE If no delivery date is given, …
5 FALSE The usual rules that apply to shopping in person also apply to distance selling
6 FALSE If you buy something without face-to-face contact, you will usually have a cooling-off period
7 TRUE you will usually have a 'cooling-off' period of seven working days
8 FALSE It lets you cancel the order for any reason
9 NOT GIVEN
10 FALSE You don't have this cancellation right: if the item is perishable, e.g. food or flowers
11 viii you are quite within your rights to … return the goods and get a full refund
12 vi You may be required to bear the cost of returning the goods
13 iii your only obligations are to make the goods accessible for collection
14 iv It would be impossible for you to do this without opening the box or bag
15 ix you need to ensure that things are of good quality and work properly
16 ii if you see that you have paid for goods you didn't buy, you can ask the card company for the money back
17 C the site … did not look particularly promising
18 B It has the potential to give us a glimpse into an unknown part of world history
19 C The dig was ordered after Aboriginal groups voiced concerns
20 B claiming that the bridge will not destroy or disturb it
21 stone They're stone artefacts
22 wild cherries Wild cherries were the main thing to be gathered in the area
23 1,440 they found 1,440 artefacts
24 cutting they're used for day-to-day living, cutting
25 National Heritage One local politician has called for the site to be National Heritage listed.
26 B inland caves were occupied
27 E Coastal rubbish pits date back only 5,000–6,000 years
28 1938 His brilliant 1938 climb
29 Three days Reinhold Messner … thought his three-day ascent 'a work of art'
30 Edward Whymper first climbed by EW in 1865
31 Bruno Brunod ran … to the summit and back in just …
32 Kilimanjaro He holds the record for the fastest ascent of Kilimanjaro
33 Two hours 28 minutes Arnold climbed Heckmair's route in just …
34 2011 that year. A few months later
35 FALSE with three companions
36 TRUE Arnold climbed without anything to catch him if he fell
37 FALSE Putting the mountain off limits to other members of the public wasn't an option
38 NOT GIVEN
39 TRUE the record for Patrouille's 53-kilometre course
40 FALSE the danger isn't much less than it was in Heckmair's day